IN THE

Resources from MOPS

Books
> Beyond Macaroni and Cheese
> A Cure for the Growly Bugs and Other Tips for Moms
> Getting Out of Your Kids' Faces and Into Their Hearts
> In the Wee Hours
> Loving and Letting Go
> Mom to Mom
> Meditations for Mothers
> A Mother's Footprints of Faith
> Ready for Kindergarten
> What Every Child Needs
> What Every Mom Needs
> When Husband and Wife Become Mom and Dad

Little Books for Busy Moms
> Boredom Busters
> Great Books to Read and Fun Things to Do with Them
> If You Ever Needed Friends, It's Now
> Juggling Tasks, Tots, and Time
> Kids' Stuff and What to Do with It
> Planes, Trains, and Automobiles ... with Kids!
> Time Out for Mom ... Ahhh Moments

Books with Drs. Henry Cloud and John Townsend
> Raising Great Kids
> Raising Great Kids for Parents of Preschoolers Workbook
> Raising Great Kids for Parents of Teenagers Workbook
> Raising Great Kids for Parents of School-Age Children Workbook

Gift Books
> God's Words of Life from the Mom's Devotional Bible
> Mommy, I Love You Just Because

Kids Books
> Little Jesus, Little Me
> My Busy, Busy Day
> See the Country, See the City
> Mommy, May I Hug the Fishes?
> Mad Maddie Maxwell
> Zachary's Zoo
> Morning, Mr. Ted
> Boxes, Boxes Everywhere
> Snug as a Bug?

Bible
> Mom's Devotional Bible

Audio
> Raising Great Kids

Curriculum
> Raising Great Kids for Parents of Preschoolers *Zondervan*Groupware™
> *(with Drs. Henry Cloud and John Townsend)*

OTHERS OF MPS.
RESCHOOLERS
because mothering matters

IN THE

Wee Hours

Up-in-the-Nighttime
Stories for Mom

COMPILED BY
MARY BETH LAGERBORG

ZONDERVAN™

GRAND RAPIDS, MICHIGAN 49530

ZONDERVAN™

In the Wee Hours
Copyright © 2001 by MOPS International, Inc.
Requests for information should be addressed to:
Zondervan, *Grand Rapids, Michigan 49530*

Library of Congress Cataloging-in-Publication Data

In the wee hours : up-in-the-nighttime stories for mom / compiled by Mary Beth Lagerborg.
    p. cm.
Includes bibliographical references.
ISBN 0-310-24024-7
    1. Mother and Child—Literary collections.   2. Motherhood—Literary collections.   3. Mothers—Literary collections.   4. Amercian literature.   I. Lagerborg, Mary Beth.
PS509.M6 I5 2001
                                     2001026745

Published in association with the literary agency of Alive Communications, Inc., 7680 Goddard Street, Suite 200, Colorado Springs, CO 80920.

Interior design by Melissa Elenbaas

Printed in the United States of America

01 02 03 04 05 06 /❖ ML/ 10 9 8 7 6 5 4 3 2 1

CONTENTS

Part Two—Starry, Starry Night: Beauty

Part Three—Star Light, Star Bright: Hope

Part Four—Night Light: Prudence

Part Five—Whistling in the Dark: Courage

Part Six—Darkest Just before Dawn: Faith

Part Seven—Morning Stars: Gratitude

FOREWORD

Wee. Odd word, isn't it, just sitting there all by itself? I think of wee as small, tiny. Or funny (whee!). Then I see the ee in wee and I experience a rush like a balloon losing air, spinning about a room in an exausting arc. Or the E on a gas gauge signaling empty.

Wee. All the above meanings rumble and tumble through my thoughts when this silly word is attached to its mate *hours*. The wee hours serve as a parentheses between night and morning, when normal human beings sleep and restore. Normal humans, I said. Not mothers.

The wee hours are a mother's unique domain where she paces, rocks, ponders ... and prays. Like a sentinel on a watch, she measures her baby's breathing. She wakens before the alarm cry. She checks foreheads for fevers and rooms for nightlights. Later in life, her job description demands attention to the phone, the gleam of headlights in the drive, and the sound of a key in the lock.

Some mothers thrive in such slices of predawn. Like nocturnal creatures, we release our imaginations to prowl about in freedom, creating hope, weaving the future. For other mothers, these wee hours launch the monster within. Our otherwise composed offerings emerge werewolf-ish: grouchy, perturbed, zealous, neurotic, martyred, and mad. We simply want to sleep and leave the darkness to itself.

However you take this journey into the wee hours, journey you must—because you are a mother. And mothers get up when others sleep because they know that even wee moments matter in mothering.

Journey into the magic waiting for you in these wee hours. Puzzle. Dream. Giggle. Find meaning for mothering.

Ready, set . . . we. Wee. Whee!

Because mothering matters,
Elisa Morgan
President, MOPS International

PREFACE

In the nighttime, when your life is in the shadows, when you can't see the piles of laundry or stacks of bills or the toys strewn on the floor, *In the Wee Hours* will bring you perspective from other women, hope to renew dreams you may have forgotten, a laugh you may need, inspiration to welcome the dawn.

Each of these stories presents a woman—or a girl—dealing with a situation. They draw upon reservoirs of pluck and courage and faith and determination that you also have deep inside you. Some of these stories will seem like they're yours—or may lend perspective to your own. Take a peek at what it was like for shy Anne Morrow Lindbergh to marry her famous husband. Or help Liz Curtis Higgs decide whether to abandon her longtime hairdresser for another. Enjoy close-up the shared mother-daughter experience of a rip-roaring thunderstorm. Experience with Anna Quindlen what it's like to negotiate the subway in New York while pregnant out to *here*.

As I look back on the years of reading bedtime stories to my children (and look forward to the years of reading stories to my grandchildren), I can see traits in my sons that are reflected in their favorite stories. Either the stories shaped my children (as they were read 163 times) or my children felt a kindred bond with the characters. For example, the son who has proved doggedly persistent through many challenges loved *The Little Engine That Could*.

So the stories you love best are no doubt telling of your life, in the daytime, when the shadows are gone. They may mirror a situation in your life or provide just the spark of encouragement that you need.

May you feast on some favorites here! May new ones meet a particular need. You'll find lots of variety, because you are not quite the same tonight—nor are your thoughts or mood—as last night. This may be the night that a short selection will be enough to set you peacefully nodding. Or you may want to savor a longer piece.

One rule: no nightmares allowed! Cast your worries to the shadows, Mom, and dream your dreams.

PART 1

Moonbeams

Love

It Will Change Your Life

By Dale Hanson Bourke

Time is running out for my friend. We are sitting at lunch when she casually mentions that she and her husband are thinking of "starting a family." What she means is that her biological clock has begun its countdown and she is being forced to consider the prospect of motherhood.

"We're taking a survey," she says, half joking. "Do you think I should have a baby?"

"It will change your life," I say carefully, keeping my tone neutral.

"I know," she says. "No more sleeping in on Saturdays, no more spontaneous vacations . . ."

But that is not what I mean at all. I look at my friend, trying to decide what to tell her.

I want her to know what she will never learn in childbirth classes. I want to tell her that the physical wounds of childbearing heal, but that becoming a mother will leave her with an emotional wound so raw that she will be forever vulnerable.

I consider warning her that she will never read a newspaper again without asking, "What if that had been my child?" That every plane crash, every fire will haunt her. That when she sees pictures of starving children, she will look at the mothers and wonder if anything could be worse than watching your child die.

I look at her carefully manicured nails and stylish suit and think she should know that no matter how sophisticated she is, becoming a mother will immediately reduce her to the primitive level of a she-bear protecting her cub. That a slightly urgent call of "Mom!" will cause her to drop a soufflé or her best crystal without a moment's hesitation. That the anger she will feel if that call came over a lost toy will be a joy she has never before experienced.

I feel I should warn her that no matter how many years she has invested in her career, she will be professionally derailed by motherhood. She might successfully arrange for childcare, but one day she will be waiting to go into an important business meeting, and she will think about her baby's sweet smell. She will have to use every ounce of discipline to keep from running home, just to make sure he is all right.

I want my friend to know that everyday routine decisions will no longer be routine. That a visit to McDonald's and a five-year-old boy's understandable desire to go to the men's room rather than the women's will become a major dilemma. That right there, in the midst of clattering trays and screaming children, issues of independence and gender identity will be weighed against the prospect that a child molester may be lurking in the restroom. I want her to know that however decisive she may be at the office, she will second-guess herself constantly as a mother.

Looking at my attractive friend, I want to assure her that eventually she will shed the pounds of pregnancy, but she will never feel the same way about herself. That her life, now so important, will be of less value to her once she has a child. That she would give it up in a moment to save her offspring, but will also begin to hope for more years, not so much to accomplish her own dreams, but to watch her child accomplish his. I want her to know that a caesarean scar or shiny stretch marks will become badges of honor.

My friend's relationship with her husband will change, I know; but not in the ways she thinks. I wish she could understand how much more you can love a man who is careful to always powder the baby or who never hesitates to play "bad guys" with his son. I think she should know that she will fall in love with her husband again for reasons she would now find very unromantic.

I wish my modern friend could sense the bond she will feel with women throughout history who have tried desperately to stop war and prejudice and drunk driving. I hope she will understand why I can think rationally about most issues, but become temporarily insane when I discuss the threat of nuclear war to my children's future.

I want to describe to my friend the exhilaration of seeing your son learn to hit a baseball. I want to capture for her the belly laugh of a baby who is touching the soft fur of a dog for the first time. I want her to taste the joy that is so real that it hurts.

My friend's quizzical look makes me realize that tears have formed in my eyes. "You'll never regret it," I say finally. Then I reach across the table, and squeezing my friend's hand, I offer a prayer for her and me and all of the mere mortal women who stumble their way into this holiest of callings.

Night Feedings

By Amy Imbody

This was not what I had expected. Every cheery chapter on Bringing Baby Home had led me to imagine that on those first few nights, when the Mommy would be exhausted and weak from her recent exertions, the solicitous Daddy could be counted on to bring the hungry baby to her—changed, blanketed—so that all she would have to do was hook 'er up and doze through nursings. This rosy picture was pleasant to contemplate, and highly theoretical.

I was later to discover that the Daddy of our house had many excellent and unique contributions to make, but Bringing Babies to Mommy for Night Feedings was not going to be one of them. This man, who could hear a cat lick its paws at 2 a.m., and waken enough to protest, could not, however, hear a baby cry in the next room.

"Honey . . ." I nudge him gently. "Honey . . . I hear the baby . . ."

A long silence from the other side of the bed.

"Honey!" I nudge again, a little harder.

". . . hmmm . . ."

"I hear the baby, Honey—I think she's hungry!"

A deep rumble from the other side of the bed. Then a slow rotation from back to side. Then a heavy shifting of husband from horizontal to vertical position. He sits hunched on the edge of the bed, head in hands. He is trying to be helpful.

"... hmm ... what is it ..."

I sit upright. "It's the baby! She's starting to cry, and I think it's time to feed her!"

A pause. "... what time is it ..."

"It's 3:32—I fed her at 12:06 but I think she's hungry again. Don't you think that sounds like her 'hungry' cry?"

A pause. "... what do you want me to do ..."

"Just get her for me, Honey—just change her diaper and bring her to me, okay?"

A pause. "... mm-hmm ..."

"And could you bring a clean burping diaper, too, Honey?"

A pause. "... where is it ..."

"Where is what?"

"... the uh ... the uh ..."

"The burping diaper?"

"... yeah ..."

"There's a stack of clean, folded burping diapers in the bottom left drawer under the changing table."

A final pause. He gathers himself and with supreme effort lumbers to his feet. He moves like a bear through the dark of the room. I am on full-alert. *Will he find the burping diapers? Will he remember to put the Desitin on her bottom? Will he think to make sure the diaper comes down below her healing umbilical cord?*

I listen for tell-tale clues to his progress. Several drawers open and close. Something falls to the floor, and it is not the baby. Unidentifiable mumblings drift my direction. Shuffling sounds approach—and lo, the Daddy comes, with Bethany, who is screaming her little lungs out in evenly paced sobs.

I am a college-educated woman: it does not take me very long to realize that there is a better way to do Night Feedings, a way that drastically reduces the interval between baby waking and baby feeding, a way that preserves the general peace of the household and actually results in more people sleeping for more hours of the night. All I have to do is get the baby myself!

SPICE

By Luci Shaw

Sentimentalists, purists, and some
Preachers, advocate marital absolutes—
Stability, a clear hierarchy for
Decision, a predictable union, unflawed,
Bland as a blank page. No wonder
It ends up flat. A truer wedding's
Grounded in paradox, answers the pull
Of the particular, grapples a score
Of rugged issues. Like horned toads
In Eden, incongruities add surprise
To a complacent landscape.

Thank heaven you're romantic and
Irascible, I'm opinionated in my
impulsiveness. Thank God we can
lean together in our failing—a rusty
trellis propping a thorned rose.

THE JUBILEE AGREEMENT

By Terry Beck

The Jubilee Agreement was signed the year I turned six. Mama had been out of sorts for weeks. Tiny wrinkles suddenly framed her gentle green eyes and her glorious auburn hair lost its luster. Nathan, her first-born, was the second-grade star of King Richard's Deli, the top soccer team in the central California league. Twice a week she loaded four-year-old Jordan, eighteen-month-old Ben, and me into the van with Nathan and his teammates. We'd traipse around the country to games, practices, and support meetings. Mama was worn ragged.

"Mothers," she told Papa after an exhausting day, "should be rewarded with an occasional vacation all to themselves. A sabbatical. A Jubilee, like in the Bible. A chance to get away." Her voice lapsed into a wistful sigh.

Papa, a giant of a man with dark hair and warm brown eyes, walked to where Mama was folding laundry.

"Would that help you shake off this confustulation, Beth?" he asked, using one of the conglomerate words from Nathan's childhood. "Then a vacation would be good. The children can take care of me for a week." He winked at us behind Mama's back. Nathan

23

and I knew life would be chaos by the end of one day without Mama. But not wanting to quench the flush of hope that brightened her cheeks, we nodded.

Unwittingly, we'd consented to the Jubilee Agreement. The terms: every three years, Mama was to take a week off. She could go wherever she wished, within a budget agreed upon by Papa.

The next month, Mama's spirits soared on a flurry of trips to the library and travel agencies. Flooded with colorful brochures offering getaways to fantastic resorts and cities across the country, she went into a frenzy of cleaning, mending, and stocking the freezer. Our neighbor, Evie, agreed to baby-sit while Papa minded his pharmacy.

Papa, Nathan, and I became morose and silent. Papa, between his continuing to romance Mama and his obligations at the store, had never spent time alone with us. Now he was having second thoughts about the whole Jubilee concept. Yet at the train station, when Mama kissed us good-bye with worried eyes and asked Papa, "Will you really be able to manage?" he commanded: "Go! We're going to be fine."

On the way home, he insisted we play his favorite game: *Morgue.* Everyone played "dead" and the last one to talk, move, or giggle won the game. Jordan, the winner of all three rounds, got to open the gift Mama left for us on the kitchen table. Ecstatic "oohs" and "aahs" greeted the two-foot-tall teddy bear pulled from the wrapping. Mama had dressed his soft brown fur in swim trunks and tennis shoes, a reminder that her destination was a health spa just south of the Mexican border.

Tucked under the bear's arm was a card adorned with a blue-gowned angel wearing a cockeyed halo and blowing a slender gold horn. Inside were two messages.

> My Precious Children,
> That I should leave you now, for this Jubilee, is hard, I know. But our separation is only for a short time. This bear symbolizes my promise that, unless an act of God intervenes, I shall come home to you. Talk to the teddy when you miss me and take care of Papa for me.
> Love, Mama

Darling John,

I'm hoping this will be a special time for you to get to know our children in a deeper way. Thank you for the gift of Jubilee. Be assured that neither time nor distance can keep me from loving you with all that I am.

Always, Beth

Buoyed by the bear (immediately christened "Teddy Talkto" by Jordan) and Mama's love, the week flew by.

Back at the station, the mother who ran from the train into our squealing midst was slimmer, tanner, and more youthful than the one we'd seen off. With her hair newly cut to frame her face, the once-too-mechanical smile now extended to twinkling eyes.

"How I missed you!" she exclaimed repeatedly, hugging us each in turn. She threw herself at Papa, who picked her up and swung her round, kissing her just like in the movies.

Mama described her trip's pampering massages, swimming, and horseback riding. But none of it impressed us as much as the inner calm she radiated. By Monday, Mama's frantic schedule hadn't changed, but her attitude had. She went about her tasks with a smile and a song.

When Mama returned from Mexico, we put away Teddy Talkto. But nine months later, as Mama and Papa went to the hospital, he reappeared—dressed in diapers and a tiny T-shirt, snuggling a purple rattle. Papa phoned us from the hospital that evening to announce Laurel Christina's safe arrival.

Ben and Jordan ran straight to Teddy Talkto with the good news. Nathan took the opportunity to explain how Papa, wanting to claim the "first dance" in each of his older four children's lives, had always ceremoniously waltzed around the house with each of us as new-born babies. Then Nathan picked up Teddy and held him cheek-to-cheek, gliding solemnly around. Entranced, we all joined in the dance.

When Mama came home from the hospital, we once again put away Teddy Talkto, but not thoughts of the special dance. We followed Papa like soldiers preparing an ambush, muffling our giggles as he waltzed 'round the house with Laurel the first day she raised her head. But he never probed our laughter. Quietly smiling, he finished the dance.

Having survived the first Jubilee, we looked forward to the second one three years later. Papa admitted his relief that Nathan and I were older and able to help more. "We'll survive your trip and the aftermath more easily this time," Papa reassured Mama. "After all, the Jubilee Agreement did not include a new baby after each homecoming." Mama patted Papa's chin: "Oh, John, what would we do without Laurel?"

We kissed Mama good-bye for Jubilee Two: forty miles of unrelenting desert in eastern Nevada reenacting a wagon train crossing of the Western Trail.

Before her car even pulled out of the driveway, we searched the house for Teddy Talkto. We found him mounted on Laurel's rocking horse, dressed as a cowboy with a ridiculously huge hat and a red bandana tied over his nose!

Our week went surprisingly smoothly. And Mama's? The weather had been unusually bad. Bleeding lips and legs blotched with bug bites were her most visible souvenirs. Hardships aside, Jubilee Two had the same magical effect on Mama as Jubilee One. She was again refreshed and renewed in her role as wife and mother. Papa's enthusiasm at her return assured us of their love for each other. The Jubilee Agreement, we concluded, was good for all of us.

The years passed. Our family took yearly vacations, but it was Mama's Jubilees that defined our lives. During Jubilee we learned not to take her for granted, as well as how to run the washing machine, load the dishwasher, and light the incinerator. We participated vicariously in Mama's travels, and her love of plotting adventure added spice to the daily routine.

Mama spent Jubilee Three at the Seattle World's Fair, leaving Teddy Talkto in a raincoat outgrown by baby Laurel (a clue as to what she expected in the Pacific Northwest). For Jubilee Four, Mama made it to Hawaii and we found Teddy Talkto sprawled on a beach towel, wearing a grass skirt and a lei.

Jubilee Five was Nathan's freshman year at the University of California in Los Angeles. This was Mama's excuse to "do" Los Angeles.

She spent Jubilee Six at a dude ranch in Wyoming and Jubilee Seven at the Grand Canyon.

The year I turned thirty, Papa joined Mama for Jubilee Eight (right after Laurel married), celebrating in Acapulco the end of the Jubilee Agreement. With all of us wed, there was no one home to see if Mama had dressed Teddy Talkto in a sombrero or mariachi outfit.

Early in the next year, Mama began to experience fatigue and stomach pains. Blood tests ordered by the doctor led to exploratory surgery. The final diagnosis of advanced cancer left us devastated. Papa, crushed, refused to talk about Mama's condition. His silence became her biggest concern. For months, Mama functioned normally, though slowly, putting her affairs in order. She spent time with each of us—laughing, crying, reminiscing, and expressing her love.

Papa waited on Mama like a devoted servant, but refused to accept the finality of her illness. Distant through the funeral and burial, he remained tearless and detached.

In the months following, every joy and victory seemed muffled without Mama there to share the celebration. Laurel broke through her grief when she gave birth to her first child, Bethany Jubilee, named for that first Jubilee that had led to Laurel's own conception. But even holding his enchanting, curly-haired grandchild did not seem to penetrate the wall of pain wrapping Papa's heart.

Hoping to lift him out of his melancholy, we agreed to congregate at the house for a traditional family Christmas that year. Nathan's wife, Melissa, organized the oldest grandchildren into teams that took turns baking cookies, making fudge, and wrapping gifts. We decorated a magnificent tree with ornaments made through the years, went caroling in the neighborhood, and attended worship services on Christmas Eve. But when Papa went to bed, we soon followed, too discouraged to rally for games.

The next morning, we gathered, somewhat subdued, for the grand gift opening. Jed, my eldest, played Santa. After we opened all the presents, he spotted one more, a large box tucked beneath the tree. There was no tag on it. Puzzled, we asked Papa to open it.

Hands trembling, he pulled out the treasured Teddy Talkto—dressed in a flowing blue robe, cockeyed halo, with a slender golden horn tucked under his arm. Nathan and I instantly recognized the angel from the card Mama had left us on her first trip. Papa covered his eyes with his hand. Jed pulled out the card in Teddy's hand. I nodded for him to read.

> My Precious Children,
> That I should leave you now for this Jubilee is hard, I know. But our separation is only for a short time. This bear symbolizes my promise that, unless an act of God intervenes, I shall come home to you. Talk to the teddy when you miss me and take care of Papa for me.
> Love, Mama

Jed looked at me questioningly. He had grown up with tales of Teddy Talkto and the Jubilee Agreement, but did not understand the significance of the card. Brushing silent tears from my eyes, I motioned him to continue.

> Darling John,
> I'm hoping this will be a special time for you to get to know our children in a deeper way. Thank you for the gift of Jubilee. Be assured that neither time nor distance can keep me from loving you with all that I am.
> Always, Beth

A groan ripped loose from somewhere deep within Papa. Shaking, tears streaming down his cheeks, he stumbled out to the kitchen. We sat in silence, until one of the children asked a question about the first Jubilee. Breaking from our sorrow, we took turns retelling the childhood stories.

Papa returned with the tray of cookies and fudge that always followed the opening of presents, smiling bravely. "Forgive me," he said, voice trembling, "for trying to deny your Mama her final Jubilee."

Then, grandchildren giggling at his feet, Papa picked up baby Bethany and gingerly waltzed her round the room.

JACI'S STORY

By Janice Chaffee

When I hear people say, "You can choose your friends, but you can't choose your relatives," it makes me sad. I'm only twenty years old and haven't been through a lot in life yet, but I'm old enough to understand the value of my family. Besides life, and the life through Jesus Christ, the best gift in the world is family.

Most of my friends describe their families as their mom, dad, brothers, sisters, and sometimes grandparents. When we say family, we mean *everybody!* Our mom, dad, all *their* brothers and sisters, all our grandparents and great-grandparents, and our brothers and sisters. Plus our cousins—first, second, and third—are just like brothers and sisters. And when anyone gets married, their husband or wife becomes family too. It's cool to have so many people in life to depend on, who look just like you, who can look at each other and say, "We definitely get this nose from our Grandma." That's what I call family! . . .

Every Christmas, my family (*all* of us!) gathers in New Mexico at Nana Kate's, my grandmother's house. That's been our tradition

---

This is the story of Christian recording artist Jaci Velasquez.

forever. Mom is one of seven children, and they all show up with their spouses and children and grandchildren. It makes for a very interesting, loud, and crowded day! A few years ago, everyone brought all their own family's gifts, but the packages took up so much space that there was absolutely no room for people! Because it was so overwhelming, we decided not to do that anymore.

We tried exchanging names one year and that didn't work either. We all want to give everybody something, even if it's just a coloring book and crayons for the littlest kids. We don't give expensive gifts, just simple ones. For us, the biggest and best gift of all is being together at Nana Kate's.

She is so amazing and so much fun we sometimes call her "Super Granny." We all love her. She plays with us and lets us get mad when she beats us at board games. She wrestles on the floor with the little kids and gets fierce in snowball fights. If someone is coming or going, they can count on getting smacked with a snowball. Then it escalates until all the adults and all the kids are in the front yard, including Nana, yelling, ducking, throwing snow, and laughing until we can't breathe.

My immediate family is usually the first to arrive in New Mexico. While we're waiting for everyone else to get there, we make luminaries, those paper bags filled with sand and a small candle. Aunts and uncles and kids make them together, four generations preparing light for Christmas. We set them around the driveway and make a design in the yard. Then after dark we light the candles and admire our handiwork.

Another of our traditions is that we all pile into a couple of cars and drive around town to see the Christmas lights. We save one big house on the edge of town for last. The owners decorate their entire hill and you can see it from miles away. Every year they add something to the incredible scene, and it's always so much fun to discover the new part and see the stuff they've had for years. I have to admit, though, that there is nothing like the luminaries—the yellowy candlelight glowing through dozens of paper bags in the darkness. I love coming home to see them, year after year.

By Christmas Eve the entire family is together. Some of them attend Mass or a program at a local church, or we all go together to a midnight service. I always love the sight of Mary riding in on a donkey and am moved at the beauty of a live baby in the manger. Sometimes, we decide to stay at home and watch a Christmas special on television, just waiting for everyone to come in so we can open presents.

Everyone's very first gift is from my grandmother—a little brown paper bag filled with an apple and an orange, nuts, and Christmas candy. There are so many bags lined up under the tree! I love those bags. They're tradition. My mom used to get one from her grandmother and now I get one from mine. I can't wait until I have children and they get one from my mom. It's a simple gift, but it represents such love.

Then mad chaos begins when we open all the rest of the gifts— oh, my gosh! The noise in the house is amazing—little kids shouting and running and people talking non-stop in Spanish and English. Of course, everyone is eating all the time and drinking eggnog topped with whipped cream and nutmeg. I don't know if that tradition is Spanish or English or German or what, but we love it! We hang out, talk, and laugh, play music and games, and eat all night long. Together—as a family.

Of course, it's inevitable that the family stories get told and retold year after year. Even though I used to get embarrassed, I couldn't wait until someone told one of "my" stories. I was about two or three when I got my first doll. It was one of those big ones, almost as big as me. I ripped open the box, but couldn't get the doll out since it was fastened down with wire. I was so happy and in such a hurry to love her, I just climbed in the box and laid down. I don't remember doing that at all, but it seems as though I do because I've heard the story so many times.

Even though I've heard the original Christmas story so many times, it's still wonderful to hear it again—the angels, the shepherds, the wise men bringing gifts to the baby in the manger. There's such comfort in knowing the story will be told again and again and that it will never change.

God promised to be faithful to all generations and He is. It's up to us to pass on the story of Christmas, just the way my family passes on the tradition of red chili on mashed potatoes. It's one thing to pass on traditions of food, but it's more important to pass on a tradition of truth that affects eternity. The younger adults and the children see the example of faith in the older generation, in mothers and fathers and aunts and uncles and brothers and sisters and cousins—first, second, or third—and take it as their own. Our tradition of lighting luminaries reminds us that Jesus came as the Light of the world. Passing out brown bags filled with fruit and candy reminds us that every gift comes from the Father of lights. When we are together, laughing and teasing and playing in the snow, we are reminded that the people of God are called a family.

It all started with the birth of a boy in a town filled with traditions. His family was small and probably quiet the night of his birth. My family is large and we're never very quiet. Our families may be different, but we both received the same thing: a baby in a manger, the perfect gift from God.

To My Dear and Loving Husband

By Anne Bradstreet

If ever two were one, then surely we.
If ever man were loved by wife, then thee;
If ever wife was happy in a man,
Compare with me, ye women, if you can.
I prize thy love more than whole mines of gold
Or all the riches that the East doth hold.
My love is such that rivers cannot quench,
Nor ought but love from thee, give recompense.
Thy love is such I can no way repay,
The heavens reward thee manifold, I pray.
Then while we live, in love let's so persevere
That when we live no more, we may live ever.

—1678

POSSESS YOUR SOUL IN PATIENCE

By Luci Shaw

Wedding poem for John and Christa

Own it. Hold your heart the way
You'd hold a live bird—your two hands
Laced to latch it in, feeling
Its feathery trembling, its fledgling
Warmth, its faint anxieties
Of protest, its heart stutter
Against the palm of one hand, a fidget
In the pull of early light.

Possess it, restless, in
The finger cage of patience. Enfold
This promise with a blue sheen
On its neck, its wings a tremor
Of small feathered bones
Until morning widens like
A window, and God opens
Your fingers and whispers, Fly!

RADIOACTIVE TOMATOES

By Chonda Pierce

Here I have lamely related to you the uneventful chronicle of two foolish children in a flat who most unwisely sacrificed for each other the greatest treasures of their house. But in a last word to the wise of these days let it be said that of all who give gifts these two were the wisest.

"The Gift of the Magi," O. Henry

Soon after David and I were married I became pregnant (surprise!), and Chera Kay was born in the winter of 1984. When she was an infant, we were living in a small apartment at a motel. Yes, a motel! David was the on-site maintenance man, and in the winter months, while Opryland was closed, I was a desk clerk. We had a great setup! The owners of the motel were like parents to us: they housed us, fed us, and when I was sick, they sent housekeeping down to run the vacuum and make the beds. We hated to leave them (and give up the little bathroom soaps). But David had an English degree and was tired of being a maintenance man. He had been offered a training position as a nursing home administrator. (I know, it wasn't exactly "in his field," but at the time, this sounded like a good opportunity. We were just trying to find our niche.) So we packed up and moved to Glasgow, Kentucky.

We borrowed some money from the bank and bought David three suits, some shirts, and a couple of ties that he could mix and match and make it appear as if he had six different outfits. With our meager savings (all $327.46!) we found a little rental house in great need of repair (but at least it had air conditioning) and moved in. We had no stove or washing machine. We had one hot plate and a toaster oven. (Thank heaven for wedding gifts!) And we bought a refrigerator for fifty dollars. We ate macaroni and cheese just about every night. (I know, I know this sounds cliché, but David did insist on Beanie Weenies for Friday nights and hot dogs for Sunday dinner.) David's paycheck barely covered the rent, the car payment, and the suit payment, leaving a few dollars left over for groceries. Here we were in a "new world" to us and with no Pampers, no television, no phone, and no friends. All we had was each other.

And our tomatoes—we grew tomatoes. I'm positive those homegrown fruits saved our lives. We planted them at the corner of the house, right beneath the drip from the air conditioner condensation drain. At first we thought maybe the dripping water had some positively charged ions or something, because the plants grew up past the windows, up to the gutters, and actually lay on the roof of the house! Later, our neighbor asked us why we planted the climbing vines instead of the bush plants. I think David told him something about a NASA experiment he was involved in.

Too bad we couldn't have grown Pampers. We had six cloth diapers that I was constantly washing out and hanging on the line to dry. If it was a rainy day, Chera Kay would wear dish towels until the diapers could dry in front of the fan. Some may think the sight of a baby crawling around with the pictures of pots and pans on her fanny is cute, but it wasn't easy trying to remember which tea towels were real tea towels and which ones were diapers. The three of us would take long walks together (once the real diapers dried, of course), sit on the back porch for hours singing and playing the guitar, laugh at the cute things Chera Kay would do or tie more twine to the tomato plants.

My mom and stepfather, Sam, drove up from Nashville just to bring us a television set. It was one of those cabinet models with a turntable and an AM/FM stereo and fancy cloth-covered hi-fi speakers mounted in each end. (I hadn't seen one like this since I was a little girl.) The television was black-and-white and the reception had this washed-out look, sort of like an x-ray—but the sound was great! We had cleared out a spot against the far wall (it took up the whole wall) and I made some popcorn on the hot plate (popcorn was cheap).

After Mom had gone back home, David and I sliced some tomatoes and prepared to watch our first evening of television in weeks.

I didn't think the picture was too washed out. And if you concentrated on one spot, the constant flipping of the vertical hold was not too distracting either, but David couldn't enjoy the show. So he took some of his old maintenance man tools, slid the cabinet out from the wall and crawled in behind the set. The last thing I remember him calling out to me was, "Tell me when this looks better!" Seconds later, there came two popping sounds: the first one came from somewhere inside the television, the other when David jumped back and hit his head on the wall. The TV screen washed out bright like a camera flash. Then the picture folded down to a thin, skinny line before shrinking to a pinpoint of light that seemed to hang right in the center of the dark green screen for days. Gray smoke puffed up from behind the set, and I heard David say, "Uh-oh."

"Oh, that's a lot better," I announced, suddenly losing my appetite for popcorn. That was the night our television set became a coffee table.

A few weeks after that, David came home for lunch and said my brother Mike had called him at work. I was to call him back. So that afternoon I carried Chera on my hip and walked to a nearby convenience store to use the pay phone. Mike and Doris, who live in Mt. Vernon, Ohio, wanted to see the baby and suggested that we meet them in Cincinnati for the weekend.

Mike said, "We can split a hotel room, eat out, and play golf the next day on a new course I've been wanting to try out. Doris is dying to see the baby. How about it?"

It sounded wonderful. But, well, "We really couldn't afford it right now...."

As big brothers sometimes do, he said, "Oh, come on. We'll take care of the weekend."

We went back and forth a few times and finally I burst into tears. "Look, we just can't do it. We don't have gas money to make the three-hour drive. Chera Kay is wearing dish towels. I'm nursing her four times a day and refueling with macaroni and cheese and radioactive tomatoes. We're doing our best to keep our heads above water. Furthermore, if we had the money to golf, we would use it to buy diapers. So the answer is NO."

Mike grew horribly silent.

Then that tone that sometimes parents take with their children—the one where concern and I'm-gonna-whoop-you-good mingle—came out as he said, "If you had just told me earlier, I'd have sent you some money!"

I knew he would. But David and I were both pretty independent. We wouldn't admit even to each other—much less to someone else—that we were both miserable! I had hated leaving Nashville, my mother, and the upcoming season at Opryland. And as for David, well, nursing home administrator trainee wasn't exactly the future he'd hoped for.

Mike ended the conversation by telling me to walk to Western Union, because he was going to wire me some money.

When David returned for the evening, I had the table set and had sliced some tomatoes and made a pot roast for supper. I was so excited with the anticipation of giving him the news of our impending trip to Cincinnati. David loves to golf, and it had been months and months since he could afford even to play Putt-Putt. So when he came in the door, I had Chera Kay dressed in her Sunday bonnet and our suitcase packed so that we could leave after supper. I yelled, "Surprise! Guess what you get to do this weekend!!!??"

David just stood there, dumbfounded. So I started blurting out our fun news: "Mike sent us some money, and we're going to eat out and stay in a motel and you and Mike are going to golf all day! And Doris is going to take Chera and me to pick out some baby clothes. Isn't that great!?!?"

David slipped into his chair at the dinner table, the blood drained from his face, causing the tomatoes to look that much brighter. "I can't play golf," he said.

"Sure you can. I know it's been awhile. And maybe you'll hook or slice or whatever, but it'll all come back to you."

"No. I mean I can't play because . . ." He began to pull some money out of his pocket, ". . . because I pawned my golf clubs today." On the table he laid out some new, folded bills: Pampers and food money.

Thirty dollars. That's what he'd gotten for the clubs. He could have played with them for years to come—could have enjoyed hour upon hour of hitting that little white ball all over the pasture. He read about golf, talked it, slept it—he even watched it on TV! But he cashed them in for two weeks worth of Pampers, more macaroni and cheese, and some Beanie Weenies.

There are moments in a marriage, I've learned, where couples can grow apart, but I've also discovered that husband and wife can grow together. I remember on Papaw's farm a pair of twisted trees that grew through an old fence. They were wrapped one around the other. At some places along the twisted trunks the fence was wedged between the barks; at other places the trunks were so meshed that I could not discern where one trunk stopped and the other began. At those points, they were as one. That was what that moment was like for us. As the money lay on the table and David was saying, "Go get the Pampers," we grew together; there was no way to tell where he ended and I began.

HOUR OF GOLD, HOUR OF LEAD

By Anne Morrow Lindbergh

To be deeply in love is, of course, a great liberating force and the most common experience that frees—or seems to free—young people. The loved one is the liberator. Ideally, both members of a couple in love free each other to new and different worlds. I was no exception to the general rule. The sheer fact of finding myself loved was unbelievable and changed my world, my feelings about life and myself. I was given confidence, strength, and almost a new character. The man I was to marry believed in me and what I could do, and consequently I found I could do more than I realized, even in that mysterious outer world that fascinated me but seemed unattainable. He opened the door to "real life" and although it frightened me, it also beckoned. I had to go.

Romance was not the deciding factor. The shimmering haze of glamour that surrounded our courtship only blurred my feelings. I distrusted it. Romance was what the world saw and applauded in our engagement. Unlike most brides-to-be, it was *I* who was congratulated, not he. Hadn't I found and captured the hero of the hour? As a gay member of the Embassy sang: "She was only an ambassador's daughter, but he was Prince of the air."

I did not see my husband-to-be as a Prince but though it was never put into words, the image was nearer to that of a knight in shining armor, with myself as his devoted page. The role of page came naturally to me. For years I had been an adoring understudy to my older sister. And I had early been cast in the role of page in a long succession of school plays, chosen no doubt for my small stature and limited acting ability. ("What ho, cup-bearer!"—"Yes, Sire, I come!")

Was this a good basis for marriage? Hardly. But perhaps it was a first step in a relationship. It was a role I could play until I grew up. I was an apprentice to someone more experienced in a world of which I knew little but which I was eager to explore. I followed; I applied myself; I learned. I leaned on another's strength until I discovered my own. It was not a bad beginning.

But there were other doors to liberation. Flying was a very tangible freedom. In those days it was beauty, adventure, discovery—the epitome of breaking into new worlds. From being earth-bound and provincial, I was given limitless horizons. From the cloistered atmosphere of books, writing, and introspection, I was freed to action. The practical work of learning to fly, of being a radio operator and navigator, of carrying my own parachute and my own "weight" as a crew member on the flights, gave me a feeling of enormous self-confidence. For the first time, I had a sense of value in the "real world" of life and action. Like the bird pushed out of the nest, I was astonished that—flapping hard—I could fly. All this was liberating.

But total freedom is never what one imagines and, in fact, hardly exists. It comes as a shock in life to learn that we usually only exchange one set of restrictions for another. The second set, however, is self-chosen, and therefore easier to accept.

The first restriction I faced was finding myself in the public eye. From the creative darkness of anonymity, a sheltered family life, and intimate communication, I was suddenly thrust into the blaze of a naked stage. Even in the first days of our courtship, the freedom of privacy was denied us. Because of the merciless exposure we lived in, it was hardly possible to get to know this stranger well enough to be sure I wanted to marry him. The abnormality of our life explains many of my doubts during the engagement period.

It is difficult to believe or even to remember how little privacy we had; how hard we struggled to be alone together. Others in the lime-light have suffered the same experiences and worse, but this was a new ordeal for me. In Mexico City, reporters waited for us at the Embassy gates, their cars and cameras set to follow us. At Cuernavaca, in the weekend house of my parents, enterprising photographers climbed up onto nearby roofs and miradors to photograph us in our garden. Disguised, we sneaked out of back doors, went to friends' houses, changed cars, and fled into the wild country of Mexico, which was then considered dangerous because of bandits. We went flying. Here at least we were not followed. After passing through the bar-rage of cameras at the flying field we could take off and leave the crowds behind, landing for a picnic on the plains—alone at last.

But total isolation is not normal life any more than total public exposure. Like criminals or illicit lovers, we avoided being seen in the world together and had to forgo the everyday pleasures of walk-ing along streets, shopping, sightseeing, eating out at restaurants or taking part in public events. Even social occasions at the Embassy or in my parents' home in Englewood, New Jersey, were not free from intrusion. Servants were offered bribes, letters were stolen, telegrams often leaked out, reporters talked to unsuspecting guests or friends and printed distorted anecdotes about our private life or, if they ran short of material, they simply invented stories.

Most restricting of all, I was warned by my husband-to-be, an intensely private person who was determined to keep intact this most private of all relationships: "Never say anything you wouldn't want shouted from the housetops, and never write anything you would mind seeing on the front page of a newspaper." The effect on me of this injunction was smothering. The lid of caution was clapped down on all spontaneous expression. I was convinced I must protect him and myself from intrusion into our private life, but what a sacrifice to make never to speak or write deeply or honestly! I, to whom an experience was not finished until it was written or shared in conversation. I, who had said in college that the most exciting thing in life was communication.

Of course, once we were married I could talk freely to my hus-band, but only in the privacy of a plane, a wilderness, or a bedroom.

And even in a hotel room, I had to be sure that the windows and the transom to the hall were closed to eavesdroppers. Besides, communication, like love, "bloweth where it listeth" and to have to confine it to one person, place, or time was to put a string on a wild bird and expect it to fly. The result was dampening for my kind of inner life. I stopped writing in my diary completely for three years, and since even letters were unsafe, I tried to write cautiously or in family language and jokes.

Our wedding on May 27, 1929, in my parents' home in Englewood, New Jersey, was kept a secret. My wedding dress was made by the local seamstress and my bouquet picked by my sister Elisabeth from the garden. Even the few friends and relatives who attended were not told until that morning. There were no photographs taken. We escaped in a borrowed car. I seem to remember lying down in the bottom while passing the crowd of reporters at the gate. We changed cars at a friend's house, drove to Long Island, and rowed out to a cabin motorboat left anchored for us near shore. We slipped out into Long Island Sound at night and headed up the coast toward Maine.

Two days later we were recognized while refueling at Block Island. For the rest of our honeymoon we were pursued by reporters and photographers in boats and planes. One man in an open boat circled around us in the harbor for seven straight hours, his wake rocking us constantly, as he shouted demands that we come out on deck and pose for him. Finally we headed out to open ocean, trailing our anchor behind. I remember the night spent on a fishing bank, out of sight of land, with cans rolling around the hold and china smashing as our boat tossed in the waves.

I was quite unprepared for this cops-and-robbers pursuit, an aspect of publicity that has become a common practice with public figures. I felt like an escaped convict. This was not freedom.

When we returned to "ordinary life"—my husband's work surveying and organizing transcontinental and intercontinental airlines—it was more acceptable. We had no private life—only public life. The launching of passenger airlines, we recognized, was of legitimate interest to the public. We went everywhere together; we posed for photographs and my husband talked to newsmen.

We had no home; we lived in hotels, planes, or other people's homes. We traveled constantly, back and forth across the United States laying out the new Transcontinental Air Transport passenger route between New York and Los Angeles, or inaugurating new Pan American Airways routes to Central and South America. We stayed in Harvey Houses, private homes, embassies and legations. I was grateful to those friends or strangers who opened their homes to us, for I realized we brought burdens with us, of extra telephone calls, invitations, press pressure, and curious sightseers. My diaries and letters attest to the generosity of the Guggenheims in New York, the Bixbys, Knights, and Robertsons in Saint Louis, the Eastlands in San Francisco, the Madduxes in Los Angeles, and countless others on our trips around the Caribbean, in the Arctic and in the Orient, who took us in and gave us a sense of security and a precious taste of private life.

It was not many months before I realized that I, who passionately desired "real life," had only exchanged the insulation of conventional upbringing, a close family circle, and a cloistered life of books for the insulation of fame, publicity, and constant travel. . . .

This is not to say I was unhappy. The letters reveal my happiness—our happiness. I was very much in love and there was (to quote a letter) "a kind of bright golden 'bloom' over everything; maybe it's just the way we feel—C. and I—when we get off together alone. All gold—" I obviously adored the flying. It was freedom and beauty and escape from crowds. It was privacy as well. There was too much noise in those early open planes to talk, but we could exchange notes. Flying also provided time alone, peace to sink down into oneself, to think, to learn poetry. (There was no one around to interrupt with magazines, snacks, or pillows in those early days.)

Thrown into a life of travel and action, I found it invigorating. Flying back and forth across the continent, stopping at small airports, meeting country crowds, gave me a new sense of the breadth and beauty of America and the warmth and vitality of people I had never met in my New England youth. To my surprise—for I had been a shy girl—I discovered I enjoyed meeting people: the pilots and their wives, the aviation personnel at the airports, who were often friends of my husband, even the strangers we took up on flights or met at trip functions. Talking to them was far easier, I found, than making conversation at the Embassy social functions. As a married woman, I had my husband at my side and developed a new confidence. "I always feel like standing up straight when he is behind me."

But I longed to gossip about these new experiences and people with my family. My reactions certainly come through the letters, but in the early years they are somewhat restrained and unnatural. I was afraid of being indiscreet. I longed to see and talk to my family as I had always done before.

My homesickness for my family now seems incredibly naïve for a young wife, and rather hard on a young husband. As the letters state, I found it difficult to believe I was married. I was happy in the new life but I missed my family terribly. How much of this is universal in the first year of marriage and how much of it was my particular problem of missing the freedom to gossip and exchange impressions with my sisters?

After a year of peripatetic living, constantly traveling, always on guard, avoiding all personal questions, speaking in discreet banalities, I longed for privacy, a home, an ordinary home. Everyone else, I thought with envy, has a home, family life, privacy, a baby.

The winter of 1929, waiting for the first baby, was not exactly a normal one. We continued our life in the air. We flew to the West Coast to supervise the construction of a plane with which my husband planned to carry on his air-route surveys. We made test flights. We flew up and down the coast. We experimented with gliding. I had already had some training in a Bird biplane. I received a gliding pilot's license after one day of instruction. We flew east across the country in our new plane, breaking the transcontinental speed record, two months before the baby was born.

Looking back with the hindsight of forty years, I feel those exploits on my part were of questionable wisdom. No doubt, since I had difficulty believing I was married, I could hardly imagine I was having a baby. All that flying around in open cockpits, being pulled off a mountaintop in a glider, and making a transcontinental record flight at what was then considered high altitudes (without oxygen) was, I now think, tempting providence. But I felt young and strong and invulnerable.

TELLING THE TRUTH

By Sheila Walsh

Barry, Christian, and I always travel together. We've done so ever since Christian was six weeks old. But in the fall of 1999, I took a three-day trip without them. We were at the end of our hectic year, and we were all tired and a bit under the weather. We had gotten back from a conference in Charlotte, North Carolina, on a Sunday night, and I was scheduled to leave for Dallas at 6:00 the next morning. Barry and I talked about whether I should break our custom and go by myself. I knew I'd be busy each day as we filmed the opening video for "Women of Faith 2000." It seemed to make more sense for everyone else to rest. My father-in-law, William, lives with us, so I felt comfortable that my boy would be fine with Daddy and Papa to take care of him.

While I was gone, I talked to Christian on the phone every morning and every evening, and sometimes at lunch as well. I had hidden three presents in different parts of the house, and each day I would tell him where to find a new one. He seemed to be doing well.

Then I got home. He was a little quiet. He told me what he had been doing, but I sensed, as mothers often do, that something was a bit off. That night as I was rocking him, I asked him if he was all right.

46

He said he was just fine. I said to him, "You know, Darling, some-times you might be angry with Mommy or Daddy, and that's all right. You can tell us."

He looked at me for a moment and then gave me his little sign that he wanted to whisper something in my ear. I bent down.

"Mommy, I'm angry with you," he whispered. "You left me."

I hugged him and told him I was sorry. I rocked him and held him tight, thanking God that children are honest enough to let us into their pain so that moms and dads can share it. When Christian fell asleep that night, I thought about what he had done and how hard it would have been for me. I don't like to let people know they've hurt me. I don't like to make myself that vulnerable. I hate being *needy*, and yet I am. We all are.

One of the biggest challenges in my marriage is to let Barry into my disappointments. I expect him just to get it—which is, of course, unfair and unrealistic. Perhaps it's not so different with God. I'm learn-ing to invite God into all my questions about him. I'm learning to crawl right up into the Father's lap and tell him that I'm angry, I'm afraid, I'm sad. We are invited to do that, you know. He will be there. He will hold us. Rather than diminishing our relationship with him, there will be a depth of intimacy born out of honesty, out of bringing our unseen self, our secret self, so full of questions and fears, to him.

A Time for Pearls

By Margaret Jensen

The Great Depression was in full swing. The cupboard was bare, and we anxiously awaited Papa's pay. Instead of giving the money to Mama, the treasurer had given the check from the church where Papa worked directly to Papa. Usually it was Mama who got the check and doled out street car tokens and an occasional nickel for a cup of coffee. Papa was noted for "giving freely all things." Walking past a jewelry shop, he saw a lovely string of pearls. At the same time, he felt the money in his pocket. Overjoyed at discovering his wealth, he purchased the pearls.

Bowing low, in great respect, he handed her the gift. "Mama, I suddenly realized I had never bought you a present. You have such a beautiful throat, you should wear pearls."

Mama never flinched. Tenderly she thanked him for the generous gift and promised to wear them always. She did! Later she told me, "There is a time and place for everything. Sometimes we need pearls more than potatoes. That was the time for pearls." Mama somehow saw that we survived until next payday.

PART 2

Starry, Starry Night

Beauty

IN THE WEE SMALL HOURS OF THE MORNING

By Cathy Conger

In the wee small hours of the morning,
'Cross my pillow moonbeams sweep,
Awake a verse, a phrase, a thought,
A nagging rhyme my mind has wrought.

Turning, tumbling, stanzas creep,
Determined to disturb my sleep
Until I rise with pad and pen
To make of them a poem then

So like a babe that comes at night,
I labor on 'til morning light.
Dawn filters through my birthing room
As life comes forth from poem's womb.

In the wee small hours of the morning
The world will be stirring soon,
But I who have birthed a poem
Will be sleeping in 'til noon.

—November 1998

HER FROZEN SOUL WAS THAWED

By Luci Shaw

I once read the 1870 journal of a prairie woman who noted about the quilts she made by hand, "I make them warm to keep my family from freezing. I make them beautiful to keep my heart from breaking." It doesn't take too much imagination to fill in the blanks of her story. Isolated during the winter months in a sod house in the vastness of the snow-sheathed prairie, her hunter husband gone for days at a time, checking his traplines, her children shut in with her to survive the frigid winters, without much nourishment for body or for soul, she turned to her own ingenuity to remedy the lack. In her quilts, their "raw-cut, uncolored edges" mirroring her own spare way of living, their colored pieces cut from scraps of calico, from worn-out clothes, she was able to create new and enchanting patterns. Under her fingers, painfully, stitch by small stitch, were formed the wedding ring and double star patterns. Her frozen soul was thawed with the beauty she herself had made from cast-offs. As Frederick Buechner has said in *Whistling in the Dark*: "Beauty is to the spirit what food is to the flesh. It fills an emptiness in you that nothing else under the sun can."

Yes, beauty is of God, the author of design and pattern and form, and we are made in his image, to respond to such loveliness with gratitude. Is it any wonder we love flowers?

PERFECT MORNINGS, PERFECT MEMORIES

By Suzanne Berne

One of my earliest memories is of being bundled up by my mother and taken outside on a snowy January night to look at the stars. I must have been four or five, still small enough for my slender mother to carry. We stood on the veranda of our house in Virginia, a heavy shawl wrapped around us both, gazing over the white fields at the sky as my mother pointed out the constellations she knew. "The North Star is the brightest star in the sky." She whispered, her warm breath wreathing my ear. "Once you find it, you can always figure out where you are." Nestled against my mother, I found this instruction both sensible and enchanting, and I have never forgotten it.

My mother liked to combine enchantment with sense whenever she wanted to make a point. "This is what morning should look like," my mother told us several times one summer, when she woke us before dawn to visit a barrier beach off Cape Cod. She would usher us through the soft gray light to where a silent old man waited to ferry us over in his narrow fishing boat. As I recall, he met us at the town landing and without a word, lifted each of us children into his boat and later onto the beach. Then my mother would lead the way across the dunes so that we could watch the sun finish rising over the water. We'd sit on a blanket in our windbreakers eating cranberry muffins and drinking hot chocolate from a Thermos, sand filling our sneakers as the day grew brighter. For miles there was no one but us. Deer ran through the eel-grass; sandpipers dashed back and forth at the shoreline, their thin black legs moving so fast they were almost invisible. The breeze smelled of salt and seaweed. "Look," my mother would say, as she pointed to raccoon prints, to a plover's nest lined with pebbles holding four beautiful spotted eggs.

Although I'm not sure she realized it at the time, my mother believed in creating memories for her daughters—a perfect morning, a glimpse of winter stars—bright pebbles to carry from the nest of childhood. It was her way of defining what she thought should matter to us. She wanted her children to love the world sensually, as she did, and to appreciate small, homely adventures. She also believed in participating in any adventure she charted out—wading barefoot in a creek hunting for crawfish, for instance. I can still recall the cool ooze of mud between my toes, the warmth of the sun on the back of my neck, and my mother, her linen skirt bunched around her knees, wading beside me, laughing at the leaf shadows dappling the water.

Perhaps because of adventures like that one, I've been fascinated by early memories and the mysterious way they color so much of the adult world. Ask my mother why she hates yogurt, and she'll tell you about drinking soured milk during the Depression on her father's farm. Ask why she likes rooms with high ceilings, and you'll probably hear about afternoons spent in the cornfields, the vault of sky above her head.

On my desk is a notebook full of early recollections I've jotted down from the biographies and memoirs I've read. Not surprisingly many of them involve mothers. One of Eudora Welty's first memories is of her mother reading to her as they sat together in a rocking chair, which "ticked in rhythm as we rocked, as though we had a cricket accompanying the story." Colette writes of her mother's garden, brilliant with "burning shades of roses, lychnis, hydrangeas, and red-hot-pokers." Virginia Woolf recalls her mother standing on a balcony in a white dressing gown, surrounded by passionflowers, "great starry blossoms, with purple streaks, and large green buds, part empty, part full."

As I glance through my notebook, what appeals to me about each of these memories is the bit of detail lacing the edges, the imaginary cricket, the burning roses, those passionflowers. These are stitches that hem past and present together, what we see when looking back. Nostalgia, after all, is our remembrance of focused attention, our romance with the particular. Without the odd glimmering detail, childhood would be a faded blur, lost to us; it might not have happened at all.

Lately I have been thinking more than usual about early memories, because I have a baby now, who one of these days will begin her own remembering. What will she recall first? Probably something entirely unpredictable—the lemony smell of her father's shaving cream, perhaps, or the roar of the coffee grinder. But maybe one wintry night I'll bring her outside to look up at the stars; or maybe one June morning we'll wake up at dawn and drive to the beach, although the trip may not be as thrilling without that silent old man and his narrow fishing boat.

As my daughter stirs in her crib nearby, I find myself planning. On a midsummer evening before bedtime, that hour when it's still light but the world has turned a dreamy blue and no child wants to go to bed, I will carry her out to the pond behind her grandmother's house so she can listen to the peep-peep of tree frogs and smell the pine breeze and watch the fireflies glint under a thumbnail moon. Just before it's time to go back inside, I'll lean down and say—something sensible, I hope. And then it will happen, the enchantment, that strange alchemy that fixes a flash of life into memory, and suddenly the whole scene will be etched, complete, hers forever, and mine, too.

Autumn Whispers

By Elizabeth Traff

Autumn whispers, "Play with me!"
I hear it in the breeze:
Colors dancing, beckoning
As they fall from the trees.

Scattered, vibrant splashes cry,
"Too soon, trees will be bare.
Now, the moment must be grasped."
I wonder if I dare.

I check to see who's watching.
I shuffle, swish and leap.
Leaves laugh as they surround me;
I bury myself deep.

Fall becomes a part of me,
Entangled in my hair.
Contented, I breathe deeply.
Fall's fragrance fills the air.

Another year is passing,
I see it in the trees.
Fall's beauty and its bounty
Amaze, restore and please.

I hope that I will never
Refuse when Autumn calls
Or fail to hear the laughter
Of Summer as it falls.

RELEARNING SIMPLICITY

By Mary Jensen

Today I'm looking for focus at Lake Hodges, which is only five minutes away. It's about as different from Walden Pond as another contained body of water could be. It's huge and stretches out in several directions like a glove made for an oddly shaped hand. The banks rise up to good-sized hills in some places, flat grassland in others.

My plan is to take out a small motorboat all by myself. I walk down the pier with a satchel over my shoulder as if this is what I always do on Wednesdays. I feel brave and strong—no one but me knows I've tucked a cellular phone in my bag just in case. . .

I back slowly out of the slip. It takes a few minutes every time to get reaccustomed to moving the tiller the right way. . . .

Whenever I'm out on the lake, everything seems simpler. The clutter in my garage is far enough away as to be nearly irrelevant; the decisions I have to make lose their immediacy; I could make some phone calls on my cell phone, but I pretend that's impossible.

Here in a boat in this calm water it's easy to dismiss the extraneous. The quiet and the solitude allow me the focus I need. I suspect we could live very simple lives in Thoreau's cabin if no one knew we were there (or was allowed in). It's easy to focus if there's nothing to disturb or distract. . . .

Out on Lake Hodges, there are only a few places to go. Although it's a big lake, I can cover it in an hour if I keep moving. I can carry only a small number of things with me, and these I choose carefully—something to read or study, something to snack on, a blanket to use as cover or cushion.

My little boat putt-putts noisily between the buoys. Now and then I see a splash out of the corner of my eyes—a fish jumping toward a miniature meal. I watch slender egrets take flight like lanky athletes rising in a pole vault. They have not much on their minds—food, shelter, nesting babies. I envy their grace, their flight, their singleness of being.

Funny, I think. Most of what I have on *my* mind is food, shelter, and "nesting babies" too. But the choices, the maintenance, the requests! Would that I could live at Lake Hodges like the egrets and limit the choices of my mind and the confusion in my soul.

And really, that's the question here. How can I nurture a tranquil soul with so many things vying for my time?

The ancient religious fathers knew that the key to tranquility was the simplicity of wanting and needing one thing—God. They were serious about the simple. And it makes me wonder, just how serious am I about wanting a still life? Am I serious enough to will and to want *one* thing—and that thing to be Christ? Am I willing for Him to be my focus? . . .

I turn my little boat toward the dock and rehearse in my mind the exact moment I need to kill the motor so it will drift gently into the slip. The sun's at my back—the same back that is cramped by having to twist around to operate the steering. Lake Hodges is calm; the egrets have settled somewhere I cannot see. My heart is still.

In a sense I've been in my own still-life painting. A few objects—a boat, a blanket, a book. A simple background—blue sky, shimmering lake, gorse-covered hills.

As I step out of the rocking boat, I'm reminded that while I can't carry Lake Hodges with me (or Walden Pond, for that matter), I can hold on to the peace in my soul. It doesn't come from water and egrets and bobbing boats; it comes from the inside, from the One who never changes.

I pull up in my driveway and walk into a house full of piles—of laundry next to the washer, of mail on the kitchen counter, of phone calls backed up on my machine. In one of my kitchen cupboards, all my spices are in a jumbled mess, the result of a frustrated attempt to find some vanilla.

Simplicity may not have a measurable effect on our kitchen cupboards. But it will always exert enormous influence on the panorama of our lives—our choices of time and priorities and focus. When God's will becomes the center of our lives, all our choices seem to line up, unbidden, in order before Him.

THERE IS NO FRIGATE LIKE A BOOK

By Emily Dickinson

There is no Frigate like a book
To take us Lands away
Nor any Coursers like a Page
Of prancing Poetry—
This Traverse may the poorest take
Without oppress of Toll—
How frugal is the Chariot
That bears the Human soul.

GARDENING AS THERAPY

By Ruth Page

It was one of those days. The morning was sunny and breezy, so by nine o'clock my wash was on the line, and some plums, with a guesser's amount of sugar, were bubbling on the stove, turning themselves into jam.

I went to the typewriter, because for once I had an idea. No need to wait and see what I wrote to find what I thought, as sometimes happens.

The phone rang . . . the dentist's office. "Where are you? You had an eight-thirty appointment." Too late. Feeling horribly apologetic and guilty, I wrote down the new appointment time in three separate places.

A horrified glance out the window on the way back to the typewriter revealed that one long clothesline had broken, and sheets were billowing along the ground and catching on the thorny multiflora roses.

By the time the sheets were pulled free and rewashed, the line fixed, and everything rehung, quite a few of the plums had grimly fastened themselves to the bottom of the pot and burned. Furiously I scooped them into the garbage (even the unstuck ones had absorbed the burnt taste), then set the scraped pot to soak with some soda and water. By this time my big idea had fled, and the typewriter just sat there, blank and waiting.

Forget it. When three things go wrong by midmorning, there's only one thing to do. Head for the garden. The beans needed weeding. Great: something to work out my resentments on. I knelt and started; the lamb's-quarters and pigweed pulled out easily, so I ripped them out angrily, in big handfuls. That felt good. After a few minutes I was enjoying the comforting feel of the soft, warm earth. I noticed the tiny beans were coming along just as they should, in elegant clusters hanging straight down.

As the weed heap grew and the row of handsome, weed-free plants extended behind me, I realized I wasn't frowning anymore; actually, I was smiling.

Two rows took an hour. The rich earth looked as inviting as heaped chocolate around the leafy green plants. Lugging baskets of weeds to the compost pile, downhill, then back up, made a nice healthy stretch after kneeling for so long. Then I carried armloads of *Boston Globes* and *Wall Street Journals* to the bean rows and laid them down in thick, overlapped mats on both sides of the rows. We even had some hay on hand to cover them. Now the bean rows were ready to have their picture taken.

The thick mulch along the row felt springy underfoot as I walked over to the carrots. I brushed my hands across their tops—there's a sensuous feel to a thick mass of feathery carrot greens. Pulling a couple of young ones, I rubbed them on my jeans and ate them. Crisp, slightly cool, sweet—my, they tasted good. As I chewed, my muscles relaxed and I reveled in the feel of the warm sun on my back. I listened a moment to a pair of robins arguing, then headed to the house.

Back to the typewriter. This time the words came readily. As I started striking the keys I realized I was grinning idiotically to myself.

Is gardening therapeutic? You bet it is.

METAMORPHOSIS

By Gloria Gaither

The spring is metamorphosing into summer,
And I can feel the dry and leathery skin
That encased me through the winter
Getting much too tight and troublesome
For comfort.
I want out!
Out into the fragrant breeze
That soon will dry the natal
Moisture
From my wings,
Out into the sun
From which I'll draw
The energy to fly.

And fly I will!
And as I soar,
I'll saturate my mind
With sounds of love and peace,
Everything that moves or breathes.
I'll smell the fragrance of the earth
And kiss the wind
And taste the brand of honey
Every blossom has to offer;
Yet I'll be sure to hear
The silence that the warm and welcome
Evening brings,
And in it I will race with shadows

Just to see which one of us
Can tiptoe in more softly
'Cross the grass.
(I'll walk so gently,
Even you won't
Hear me pass.)

And knowing as I do
The days can't last,
That winter will return too soon,
I'll do and hear and think
And taste it all!
I'll store up multicolor memories
To take me through
The long, gray days
Of winter.

THE CREEK

By Anna Frances Lipinski

Winding down and around our hilly woods we have a creek. It spans three sides of our home like a lucky horseshoe. This creek shares a warm place in my heart and plays a large part in building sweet memories.

When my older children were young, we'd round up all our toy boats first thing in the morning and head for the creek, a deck of cards in my pocket. We would give each boat dignity by attaching kings and queens to their prows, and then set them free after christening them with my coffee. We'd race along the bank to watch their progress, and retire or rescue those which wrecked or sank. Cheering on the last two remaining boats, we'd snatch them up just in time, just before they would drift under the road.

We'd stretch out in the long, fragrant grass to rest, idly talking and skipping stones. Sometimes we'd catch minnows.

I can still delight in the joyful absence of time pressures: no rules, the pretending and playing of sailor's duels. The children could hardly believe that their mother could be so carefree, wild, and wet! We'd have to go wading, and who could resist "falling" in? Or pulling them down with me? It was an ecstasy of splashing, wiggling, and laughing.

In the friendly warmth of noon we'd race home, hugging our closeness, our fun, tightly in our hearts. I rue the day those teenagers will think they've outgrown such simplicity. After all, I haven't. I'm still making the same kinds of memories with their younger siblings, still holding them in my heart, eternally embraced, just as the creek embraces our home and our lives.

CELESTIAL SYMPHONY

By Cathy Conger

Laying here in the dark,
Hearing nothing but the
Fwup, fwup, fwup of the ceiling fan,
I listen to Mama and Daddy's
Soft voices across the hall.

"You asleep?" Daddy says.
"Too hot. Wish it would storm," Mama says.
"Could be. Blackflies were biting all day
and the stock has been edgy.
Good storm would cut this heat," Daddy says.
"Think I'll go down and watch for it," Mama says.

All is quiet in the stifling darkness
Save the fwup, fwup, fwup of the fan
And Daddy's rhythmic snoring.
Screen door squeaks.
I pad downstairs and peer out at Mama
Swinging back and forth on the old porch swing.

There in the moonlight, is my Mama
In her nightdress, her hair all curled
Around her face from the dampness,
Her bare feet pushing the swing to and fro.

"What are you doing, Mama?"
"Too hot to sleep."
"Can I sit with you, Mama?"

"Come and watch. God is fixing to conduct a symphony."
"It's so still, Mama.
No wind, no stars, no crickets."
"Crawl up here by me and watch the sky.
We're going to see God tonight."

Mama's arm around me,
Swinging and watching for God,
The air stirs a little,
Feeling soft against my face,
Like passing through a spider's web.

Far over the shadowy fields,
The horizon lights up like a stage,
Flashing to the west, vanishing in the east,
Then flashing again.
Backlit by bursts of heat lightening,
A shifting flotilla of black clouds
Glides across the moon.

The cicadas stop to hold their breath,
Tensing for the thunder.
Through the rustle of the tall pines
A rumble comes back from the distance.
"It's coming. Are you watching?" Mama whispers.

Jagged lightening splits the sky,
Its CRACK lacerating the night.
I am afraid of the ugly heaven, rolling, thrashing.
The deep thunder comes rumbling down our road like a
     freight train.
I grab for Mama's hand.
"Hold tight," she says, "Listen for the wind."

The wind makes her grand entrance across the meadow.
Whooshing it comes, through the willows,
Madly ringing the wind chimes on the porch railing,
Wildly twisting the tree swing,
A cracking, whooshing, flashing symphony.

Out of the storm comes the rain, brown and savage,
Hurling itself to the ground
With the rage of an untamed flood.
Rivers pour from the gutters,
Eddying in muddy pools on the path.

Soaking sheets of rain pelt
Against our bare skin.
"Mama, I'm getting soaked."
"Glorious," she laughs and
scoops me into her arms.
Cheek to cheek we press our faces
Into the cold, stinging torrent,
And, all at once, I am not afraid.

I am not afraid.
In the crashing, flashing, soaking,
I am not afraid.
Mama's face glows like she is hearing a celestial symphony,
A master concerto from the courts of heaven itself.

Crashing, flashing, soaking, fading,
The storm moves on to the east,
Becoming only a distant decrescendo.
Clouds of steam smolder on the asphalt road.
Mama pulls me close to her beating heart.
"Ssh," she says. "Listen for the Amen."

A night bird cries and the cicadas
Begin their percussion again.
Sitting so still I dare not breathe,
I hear the symphony echo in my mind.
Then it is gone quick as that
Leaving us the applause
Of a million, glittering stars.

Mama and I, we saw God tonight
And I was not afraid.

—September 1998

BEING A KEEPER

By Ingrid Trobisch

Everything in my three-story house has a story. It is bulging with memorabilia, framed photographs, and desks or tables holding an array of scrapbooks and journals. Nearly every room has at least one cozy corner where I drink tea with friends and neighbors, tell stories to my grandchildren, or write letters to people far away.

In spite of a busy schedule, I make time each week to organize my writing tasks, keep cobwebs off the books, and refill my vases with a few posies, from the garden in summer, the grocery store in winter. When my grandson visits, he always wants to come into my library-office downstairs to have his good-night story. "Ingma," he said one time, "I love this room; there are so many things to see."

The things in my home are not collector's junk, the result of hoarding or cocooning; they are my lifeblood. "Just throw it away" people might say of certain objects, broken and mended. But because these things have been wounded in action, they are the more precious to me.

Brokenness is a symbol of some new value. A crack or chip or missing piece denotes that someone touched this, someone used it once upon a time. Each patch or dent says, there is a story here: another chapter in the context of our family history. . . .

Keeping is a gift of celebrating family. I often think of a woman as a steadfast rock in the middle of a stream flowing all around her. On the edge of life and death, whatever comes her way, not knowing what will come next, she finds a way to stabilize, to hold her place, to create an island of security as the tides and currents change. She keeps the faith and keeps the things that give her family a sense of continuity.

I didn't always have a house with well-furnished rooms: as a single woman I studied for two years in Paris, living in a small flat. Even there I surrounded myself with meaningful reminders of my pioneer roots in the United States: my Swedish grandmother's hand-sewn quilt, photographs of our home, my brothers and sisters and pets. Each new friend I made abroad brought sweet new memories. I placed picture cards in frames and decorated with fresh fruit and flowers from the marketplace.

After marriage, Walter and I started off in a thatched-roof hut close to a dusty African village. Our days were full, taking care of practical, spiritual, and sometimes medical needs of villagers. Our lives were geared around basic necessities. But we did have a nice picture to look at and a china cup and saucer for tea. It was the meaning we gave to things we did have that enriched our sense of place.

We made sure we had good books in different languages and some kind of music. We had a little wind-up phonograph with three records we'd rotate and a small pump organ. When we were able to get other instruments, Walter started a family orchestra. And always we had the stars. Each evening at dusk we would sit outside and watch them twinkle, fall, or move across the sky.

Many years later in Missouri, having raised our family after Walter died, I was given gifts of one vase after another. Friends knew my love for flowers, but I began to feel there was more meaning in the gifts. I looked deeper and realized I was chosen just to be a vessel, a keeper, and to hold the treasure of family and legacy brought down the years.

PART 3

Star Light, Star Bright

Hope

"HOPE" IS THE THING WITH FEATHERS

By Emily Dickinson

"Hope" is the thing with feathers—
That perches in the soul—
And sings the tune without the words—
And never stops—at all—

And sweetest—in the Gale—is heard—
And sore must be the storm—
That could abash the little Bird
That kept so many warm—

I've heard it in the chillest land—
And on the strangest Sea—
Yet, never, in Extremity,
It asked a crumb—of Me.

TAG SALE

By Anna Quindlen

There is nothing like a tag sale to force you to confront the hard choices in life. To junk the class notes from Introduction to Psychology and give away the trunk that houses them; to stare with hard, unromantic eyes at the cake plate your husband's great-aunt gave you as a wedding present and tote it out to the car; to look upon a size 8 suit and accept for all time that the body it fits is no longer yours—these things mark milestones, besides providing much-needed closet space.

The nursery school is having a tag sale. The school hall is filled with merchandise: bad afghans, ill-conceived table lamps, remaindered books. Amid it all are the artifacts of those families that consider themselves complete. There is a changing table, an assortment of stretch suits in pastel colors, a crop of crib bumpers. Tag sales are a godsend when the gestating is through; there is nothing more cumbersome or superfluous than a crib around the house when your former babies are out tearing up the playground, their T-shirts mottled with ice cream, dirt, and a bit of blood.

I know this because the top floor of my house is filled with items gathering dust, with down-at-the-heel walkers and baby gates and snowsuits size 9 months. They are not going to the tag sale. I have looked and looked at them, dumped boxes of old overalls onto the floor and then packed them up again. The tag sale makes clear to me, more clear than watching my kids sleep or explaining to them why llamas spit, that I am not ready to say I am finished with having babies. It may be that I will never have more than these two children, for reasons logical or biological. And certainly, they would be sufficient for me. But if I give away the baby things, I am giving away a part of my life that I am not yet ready to relinquish.

It is so seductive, this part, this making someone out of nothing. It feels so important, and so powerful, which is one of the reasons young girls who feel unimportant and powerless so often embrace it, without a thought to all the work and trouble that comes later. There is a lot of work and trouble, and that is why so many of my friends are happy to call a halt to their baby making. Ecstatic to have them, ecstatic to have it over with, they have pushed the playpen with glee into the back of someone else's van, gone to their tubal ligations and vasectomies with great happiness. Time to move on.

I am rotten at moving on. There was a time right after college when I gave lots of odd little parties, with not enough chairs and people sitting on the floor and food like Welsh rarebit or chipped beef. What I really needed was a chafing dish with a little candle underneath to keep all this slop warm, but I could not buy one. I was convinced that if I bought a chafing dish, it would somehow mean I would never get married. A chafing dish is a wedding present. (In fact, I got three as wedding presents. I used one once. I don't prepare chafing-dish meals anymore. I gave one dish to the tag sale last year. I am keeping the two others in case my kids want to have Welsh rarebit parties after they go skating on cold winter days when they are teenagers. But don't hold your breath.)

Now, I cannot get past the changing pads and the diaper bags. This is not about possessions; I could give away all my baby things and have another baby anyway. It is about what the possessions represent. Last year, someone turned over a portable typewriter to the tag sale, telling herself once and for all that she was never going to be a novelist. It was a shabby typewriter and brought five dollars;

only five dollars for what had once been an open door, a possibility, the turn of the kaleidoscope that could alter the pattern of someone's life forever. Then it was put up for sale, and it was nothing but a typewriter in a pale-blue case.

I don't see so many open doors anymore, so many ways to change the pattern, alter my life and the world. I don't want a divorce, and I don't want to move. I have reluctantly accepted the fact that I am not going to follow any alternative career paths, that I am not going to medical school. But I want to leave this particular door to the future open. Some of the women I know are further along; they are convinced that they have stopped at two children, or three, or one, happy and content. And yet ... and yet. "I sometimes still think about it," one woman said the other day, amid the perpetual chaos of her living room. "And then I think that I still can if I want to." Then she laid the flat of her hand on her abdomen, which will never be taut again.

Knowing that I still can, knowing that I might, knowing that I will: these are all very different things. I will be thirty-five-years old this summer. Someday a time will come when the apparatus that has worked so well will no longer work for me. For all I know, that time came last month, or will come this year, or will not come for a long, long time. But that will be an ending reached without my acquiescence. This one requires my cooperation. And as I look into a box of crib sheets, yellow with milk stains, yellowing just a bit with age, I know that I cannot cooperate right now. I have a feeling of possibility within me that means too much to give away. I could use the closet space, but right now it is something else I need much, much more.

GOD REMEMBERS

By Elisa Morgan

Shhhh ... Eva's Sleeping! The words were stitched across a tiny pink rosebud pillow, designed to be hung on the closed door while my first baby napped. Rarely had it been utilized for its intended purpose. Instead, it had become a doll pillow, a jewelry cushion and even a bath sponge.

Now my almost-middle-school daughter presented it to me. "Mom, I want to keep this in my memory box." I noted a yellow spot and a chocolate smudge and wondered why she'd chosen to keep this dilapidated emblem of childhood. Whatever her reason, I decided it needed washing. Afterward, it sat atop the washer and endured my shoving it about while awaiting its transfer to the basement box. Days passed. Preferring this reminder of my child's infancy, I avoided my task.

Then came 6th-grade orientation. Eva donned her new denim shorts and T-shirt and cracked her knuckles while we drove to her new school along with her 2,000-some new school siblings. "Intimidating" was an understatement.

We stood in one line for PE uniforms, another for school supplies, another for fee payment, and yet another for lunch credits. At last we stood in the scheduling line. *Finally,* I thought, *"Meet the Teacher."* For every year of Eva's school life I had prayed for God's selection of her teacher—for one who would help her learn, respect her personhood and develop her potential. In kindergarten my prayers were rewarded with a Christian woman who called Eva her "very special sister in Jesus." In 4th grade a cheerleader teacher encouraged Eva through some teetery moments. The next year, Eva had endured an unresponsive, introverted teacher—preparation for future tough spots.

"Dear Jesus, please provide a decent teacher for Eva's first year of middle school . . . pullleeeeeez!!!!"

As we came to the front of the scheduling line I discovered that there was no teacher to meet. We were greeted by a secretary, given a computerized printout in a code I couldn't decipher, and Eva was told to show up the next day in 2-2A.

No way. That wouldn't do for "Meet the Teacher." What was God doing? I took my daughter (who only complied because bewilderment won out over embarrassment) and went in search of a teacher to meet—in the vicinity of 2-2A. At last I came upon a small contingency of teachers having a planning meeting. Eureka!

"Does anyone in here have Eva Morgan in their class?" I bellowed from the doorway while Eva shrank into the hall lockers. A woman rose and joined us. After a few pleasantries, she paused, staring intently at me.

"Do you remember me?" she asked. I was stumped. "I'm Shelly Miller," she explained. "I used to be in a young marrieds' Sunday-school class with you years ago—before you had Eva. I prayed for you all while you waited for your adoption . . . and I made a little pink pillow for her. Do you remember? It said, 'Shhhh . . . Eva's Sleeping.'"

I looked at Eva, who was peering curiously at Mrs. Miller, the seamstress who'd created her beloved pillow.

Did I remember? Perhaps that was the wrong question. Perhaps the right question was, did I believe that God remembered?

In Isaiah 49:15–16 God responded to Israel's concern that God had forgotten his people: "Can a mother forget the baby at her breast and have no compassion on the child she has borne? Though she may forget, I will not forget you! See, I have engraved you on the palms of my hands."

Here God refers to the names of the tribes of Israel that were engraved on stones and fastened to the ephod worn by the high priest. He comforts his people by telling them he has carved their very names on his heart!

And God comforted me by reminding me that when Eva was a baby, a woman had stitched her name on a pink rosebud pillow, and 11 years later that woman would become Eva's teacher. Each year as I pray for God's selection of my children's teachers, I remind myself that God remembers.

THE STORY OF MY LIFE

By Helen Keller

The most important day I remember in all my life is the one on which my teacher, Anne Mansfield Sullivan, came to me. I am filled with wonder when I consider the immeasurable contrasts between the two lives which it connects. It was the third of March, 1887, three months before I was seven years old.

On the afternoon of that eventful day, I stood on the porch, dumb, expectant. I guessed vaguely from my mother's signs and from the hurrying to and fro in the house that something unusual was about to happen, so I went to the door and waited on the steps. The afternoon sun penetrated the mass of honeysuckle that covered the porch, and fell on my upturned face. My fingers lingered almost unconsciously on the familiar leaves and blossoms which had just come forth to greet the sweet southern spring. I did not know what the future held of marvel or surprise for me. Anger and bitterness had preyed upon me continually for weeks and a deep languor had succeeded this passionate struggle. . . .

I felt approaching footsteps. I stretched out my hand as I supposed to my mother. Someone took it, and I was caught up and held close in the arms of her who had come to reveal all things to me, and, more than all things else, to love me.

The morning after my teacher came she led me into her room and gave me a doll. The little blind children at the Perkins Institution had sent it and Laura Bridgman had dressed it; but I did not know this until afterward. When I had played with it a little while, Miss Sullivan slowly spelled into my hand the word "d-o-l-l." I was at once interested in this finger play and tried to imitate it. When I finally succeeded in making the letters correctly I was flushed with childish pleasure and pride. Running downstairs to my mother I held up my hand and made the letters for doll. I did not know that I was spelling a word or even that words existed; I was simply making my fingers go in monkey-like imitation. In the days that followed I learned to spell in this uncomprehending way a great many words, among them *pin, hat, cup* and a few verbs like *sit, stand* and *walk*. But my teacher had been with me several weeks before I understood that everything has a name.

One day, while I was playing with my new doll, Miss Sullivan put my big rag doll into my lap also, spelled "d-o-l-l" and tried to make me understand that "d-o-l-l" applied to both. Earlier in the day we had had a tussle over the words "m-u-g" and "w-a-t-e-r." Miss Sullivan had tried to impress it upon me that "m-u-g" is *mug* and that "w-a-t-e-r" is *water,* but I persisted in confounding the two. In despair she had dropped the subject for the time, only to renew it at the first opportunity. I became impatient at her repeated attempts and, seizing the new doll, I dashed it upon the floor. I was keenly delighted when I felt the fragments of the broken doll at my feet. Neither sorrow nor regret followed my passionate outburst. I had not loved the doll. In the still, dark world in which I lived there was no strong sentiment or tenderness. I felt my teacher sweep the fragments to one side of the hearth, and I had a sense of satisfaction that the cause of my discomfort was removed. She brought me my hat, and I knew I was going out into the warm sunshine. This thought, if a wordless sensation may be called a thought, made me hop and skip with pleasure.

We walked down the path to the well-house, attracted by the fragrance of the honeysuckle with which it was covered. Someone was drawing water and my teacher placed my hand under the spout. As the cool stream gushed over one hand she spelled into the other the word *water*, first slowly, then rapidly. I stood still, my whole attention fixed upon the motions of her fingers. Suddenly I felt a misty consciousness as of something forgotten—a thrill of returning thought; and somehow the mystery of language was revealed to me. I knew then that "w-a-t-e-r" meant the wonderful cool something that was flowing over my hand. That living word awakened my soul, gave it light, hope, joy, set it free! There were barriers still, it is true, but barriers that could in time be swept away.

I left the well-house eager to learn. Everything had a name, and each name gave birth to a new thought. As we returned to the house every object which I touched seemed to quiver with life. That was because I saw everything with the strange, new sight that had come to me. On entering the door I remembered the doll I had broken. I felt my way to the hearth and picked up the pieces. I tried vainly to put them together. Then my eyes filled with tears; for I realized what I had done, and for the first time I felt repentance and sorrow.

I learned a great many new words that day. I do not remember what they all were; but I do know that *mother, father, sister, teacher* were among them—words that were to make the world blossom for me, "like Aaron's rod, with flowers." It would have been difficult to find a happier child than I was as I lay in my crib at the close of that eventful day and lived over the joys it had brought me, and for the first time longed for a new day to come.

CiNCiNNATi!

By Amy Imbody

Cincinnati! Tall towers, expensive hotels, young urban professionals impeccably dressed, intense, purposeful. In the midst of this company I feel frumpy. My denim skirt and T-shirt, my white socks and sneakers label me as a small-town mom, the spouse who got to come along.

I have never been to one of these classy corporate events. I am all a-flutter. (You would never guess that in my youth I had ridden camels, schooled with prime ministers' sons, and ordered hors d'oeuvres.) I suck in my abdominals, thrust back my shoulders and try for the quick, confident stride of the Career Woman. This is not easy, because actually I am lugging a large red cooler through the foyer of the Omni Netherlands Hotel, and the thing is getting heavy. It is packed with lunch meat, cheese, yogurt, rolls, and the smallest jar of mayo I could find at Food City. Armed with these provisions, I hope to curtail the cost of my presence. (The Director for Advancement travels all-expenses-paid; his wife does not.)

Wending my way through the opulent lobby, I glance around at the busy executives. Heels clicking on the marble floor, they are all going somewhere. And so am I: to the Annual National Meeting!

My only known responsibility is to be generally useful. I have no idea how to accomplish this, but I am willing, and my mind flirts with appealing images . . . *graciously I greet the keynote speaker, instantly putting him at ease with my warmth and humor . . . serenely I direct befuddled delegates to Salon M, or to the Pavilion. . . .*

On the elevator up, the bellboy greets me respectfully. (*He thinks I'm one of Them!* I feel suddenly guilty, shy—an impostor!)

We reach the 29th floor—the top—and I hear myself chattering: "Oh, isn't this beautiful! Oh, what a classy place! Oh, look at the view!" I am a backyard daisy in the midst of orchids. I feel my plainness keenly—have I brought the right clothes? Do I *own* the right clothes?

I park my red cooler on the plush mauve carpet. This room exudes elegance. Cherry furnishings gleam beneath tasteful art deco prints. A large TV hides itself discreetly behind richly polished cabinet doors. There is no plastic in the place; all is glass and wood and burgundy upholstery.

In the closet I discover—an ironing board! Oh, blessed familiar object in this foreign land! And yes, as a matter of fact, all his shirts are indeed very wrinkled from their six hours' journey in the trunk of the car—and yes, the pants are lacking the appropriate crisp crease, and so . . .

I commence to make the crooked straight and the rough places plain. With experienced hand, I smooth rumpled surfaces, refreshing those things that had started to sag. Menial work, but it has its own joys. And in this simple, domestic act, I settle my soul, and remember who I am.

I DWELL IN POSSIBILITY

By Emily Dickinson

I dwell in Possibility—
A fairer House than Prose—
More numerous of Windows—
Superior—for Doors—

Of Chambers as the Cedars—
Impregnable of Eye—
And for an Everlasting Roof
The Gambrels of the Sky—

Of Visitors—the fairest—
For Occupation—This—
The spreading wide my narrow Hands
To gather Paradise—

THE BOMBING
OF NEWPORT BEACH

By Liz Curtis Higgs

February 1993. Newport Beach, California. The National Speakers Association, my peer group, was gathered for their winter educational workshop, and I was invited to be their Saturday evening speaker.

Big honor. Big blessing. Big ego alert.

Several details contributed to the outcome of this particular evening. For starters, I spoke in Columbus, Ohio, that same morning, and so had to fly out at 1:00 p.m. for the West Coast, hoping and praying my flight would land on time. I arrived at 5:00 with the main event just two hours away and my nerves stretched to the limit. Toss in a three-hour time change and a little jet lag for good measure, and you get some sense of my level of energy at this point. But it gets worse.

The huge meal (for some, with wine) took a l-o-n-g time to serve. Beef—heavy, sleep-inducing beef—was on the menu. And baked potatoes. And cheesecake. Zzzzzzz.

A thirty-minute slide presentation of fine art preceded my program. Oh, that perked people right up.

It was late—well after 9:00—when I stepped on the stage. By my body clock, it was midnight, as it was for many attendees.

The room was too dark, with large mirrored posts blocking both my view and theirs. Everywhere I looked, I saw Liz, and Liz looked nervous.

The five hundred attendees were, for the most part, speakers, fully capable of doing what I was about to do, and anxious to see why I was invited to do so instead of them.

If you are, say, a salesperson, this would be like having five hundred other reps standing around watching you make a sales pitch while talking among themselves—"I wouldn't do it that way, would you? Gee, I'd never have said that."

You get the idea. Pressure City.

If it sounds like I'm making excuses, you're absolutely right. Even though I'd prayed, prepared, and practiced, I laid an egg in Newport Beach. It was the longest hour I've ever spent on the platform. The few times folks did laugh, it had a strained, let's-help-her-out quality.

Groan.

One of the veterans of our association was sitting right in front of me, fast asleep, snoring away. (If I'd had a pocketful of mini-marshmallows, I'd have tossed them at his teeth like beanbags at a clown face.)

There is no death like dying on the platform. I could feel my hair turning gray as I spoke. Everywhere I looked, I saw mirrored images of myself. Bombing.

When, blessedly, I finished the last word, the audience leaped to their feet—and ran out the door. I'd hoped for a standing ovation; this was more like a running ovation. I made a beeline for my room, where I collapsed on the bed, crying like a baby.

It was 2:00 a.m. in Louisville, so I couldn't even call Bill for moral support.

Can you feel my pain?

I'd wanted to give them a performance they would never forget. Sure enough, I had.

Monday morning back in Kentucky, the phone in my office started ringing with words of encouragement from my peers.

"Liz, it wasn't that bad."

"I think people were just tired."

"I'd give you a 12, but the audience was a 4."

Nice try, but I knew the truth: On a scale of 1 to 10, I was the one who deserved the 4. Comedian David Brenner says when you do humor, you can't get good without bombing. But, David, did it have to be that night?!

I was licking my wounds in Louisville, certain that I'd never show my face at another Association gathering again, when the unthinkable happened. The program chair for the big National Convention in Washington, D.C., called and asked me to do a program to kick off the whole event.

I was stunned to silence. The committee members must not have been in Newport Beach.

The obvious solution was to say no thanks, but it's such an honor to be asked that speakers almost never refuse.

My heart was in my throat (or was it my shoes?). I needed help and fast, so I faxed a dear friend of mine, Rosita Perez, a consummate pro in the speaking business and the one who'd introduced me that fateful night.

"Rosita," I wrote, "how am I going to get back up on the platform? You were in Newport Beach, you saw me bomb, what am I going to do?"

She faxed me back. "Liz, you did not bomb, it just wasn't magic." (Rosita is a motivational speaker. They say things like that.) Her fax went on, "Let me ask you something: Do you like Dustin Hoffman?"

I'm thinking, *Dustin Hoffman?! Was he in Newport Beach?*

Her fax continued. "He's a brilliant actor, yes? Award-winning, an incredible talent, a Hollywood legend, yes?"

Yes, yes.

"Did you see him in *Ishtar?*"

Oh, yes, I'd seen *Ishtar,* back when I reviewed movies for a local radio station. I declared it the single worst movie I'd ever paid money to see. That distinction still stands. Forty million dollars, Warren Beatty, Dustin Hoffman—a bomb.

A big bomb.

In fact, one of my favorite cartoons from *The Far Side* showed a video store in Hades, with nothing on the shelves but *Ishtar, Ishtar, Ishtar. . . .*

"So, Liz," her fax concluded, "if Dustin Hoffman can survive an *Ishtar* in his career and come back and win an Oscar for Best Actor in *Rain Man,* can't you get back up on that platform?"

The woman had me there. The more I thought about it, the more excited I got. Yes, I would get back up on that horse, and if I fell off again, at least I knew I could survive.

Inspired by her words, I sat down at my computer and created a graphic reminder of my meaningful discovery:

ISHTAR HAPPENS.

It happened to Dustin, it happened to me in Newport Beach, and when/if it happens to you, now you'll be ready. There's a Japanese proverb that says, "When you stumble, don't get up empty-handed." Indeed, if you stand up with your head full of wisdom, your heart full of laughter, and your arms full of encouraging words like Rosita's, who knows what might happen.

Are you wondering what happened in Washington, D.C.? I marched into that meeting room full of my peers, with my ISHTAR HAPPENS sign safely tucked in the back of my notebook to remind me that failing beats not trying, every time. And on a scale of 1 to 10, it was . . . well, I'll sound like I'm bragging if I say a 15, so I'll simply tell you what a delight it was to call Bill and say, "Ta-da!"

What a relief.

God doesn't have Ishtar days, but he understands them only too well. That's why he gave us laughter, so we can survive them with our sense of humor and confidence intact.

MIXED PAINTS

By Mary Cooper Feliz

A rotten day was taking a turn for the worse for my six-year-old. Jim had grown an inch in the last month, and his muscles and emotions were struggling to catch up. Kindergarten was ending, classroom decorations were being taken down, and the uncharted adventures of first grade were looming in a terrifying manner.

After being chased by kindergarten girls who tore his shirt and kissed him, he came home to find his little brother had broken his favorite model car. He was mad at the world, and working hard to make the world mad at him.

Sent to bed early, he refused his usual story time, and rejected every audio-tape as "stupid." Some time later, he was still awake. "Are you still feeling rotten?" I asked. "Uh huh," he growled, face turned toward the wall. "Do you feel messy on the inside?"

"Yup," he answered, seeming a little less angry.

I talked with him about how hard it is to be six, to be finishing a school year, to have your best friend move away, and not know what's going to happen. We talked about how hard it is when you're growing so fast on the outside that your insides don't have time to catch up.

I said I understood, and that everyone—even grownups—felt that way. "I don't know a cure." I told him. "But I do know that it's a perfectly normal part of growing up. It doesn't usually last very long, but it sure is awful while it lasts." By now he felt comfortable enough to tentatively snuggle closer.

"And you know, even though you feel rotten, it doesn't mean you're a rotten person." That brought a big sigh of relief.

"For thousands of years, as long as there have been people, kids and grownups have felt that way," I said. "And in all that time, no one has come up with a good way to explain how it feels."

Complete astonishment filled the face of my six-year-old. "How come?" he wondered. "Oh, they've tried," I answered. "Some people say that they feel itchy on the inside. Other people describe it as being messy. Sometimes people say they're 'out of kilter,' like a top that has been spinning and starts to wobble when it slows down."

"Do you think anyone will ever describe it right, Mom?"

"Maybe you will be the first."

Silence.

"Well, it's kind of like all my nice feelings are beautiful bright new colors of paints. Around the edges of my insides, they are still like that, but in the middle they are that ugly brown, green, muddy color that paints get when they get all mixed up. I hate that color."

I told him that was the best explanation I'd ever heard. That night Jim slept without nightmares. Over the next few days he told me the circle of ugly colors was getting smaller and smaller, and we were able to talk about things he could do if it started to grow again.

Since then, the paint box idea has become a useful shorthand for us. Although we live in a generally happy household, it's helped our whole family to talk about complicated emotions in an easy way. Instead of "Are you mad at me?" or "Everything OK?" grumpy people in our house get a knowing "Got that painty feeling?" Sometimes it can bring a glimmer of a smile that can help a rotten mood. But even when that doesn't happen, it still lets the prickly person know that he or she is loved, recognized, and understood. It can help when people, like paints, get all mixed up.

How Wilma "Younged"

By Valerie Bell

I enjoy watching the movies of our family from my own childhood. But it never ceases to amaze me how much older my mother, Wilma, looked when we were children than how she looked when she was actually older. Her childhood had been difficult. Her father was an alcoholic, and her mother struggled to provide for her children. My mother dragged a lot of sadness into her adult life.

But when I see pictures taken later of my mother, something strikes me. Her later years were much better than her early ones. She lost weight; she colored her gray hair; she traveled; she was a social butterfly; she learned the magic of makeup; and although she had never had the opportunity to go to college, she self-educated. She laughed more. She enjoyed more. She became accomplished. (She received an honorary doctorate for her poetry.) She dressed better. The pictures of her taken in her sixties are so much more attractive than the dowdy ones of her taken in her early forties. She definitely "younged." I know no other way to describe her process of advancing through the years.

Let me explain that no fountain of youth or secret herbal potion can be credited with my mother's change. She did not undergo a face-lift. She had never heard of an antioxidant. Her "younging" was a job performed totally and completely by her spirit. It was exclusively an interior job. Her soul seemed to rid itself of a lot of baggage along the way. She traveled those last years of her life with a blitheness of spirit that amazed and sometimes worried us. She broke her leg riding a bicycle. After my father died, she fell madly and passionately into the kind of love you would expect from a much younger woman. She reveled in attending lectures and learning new things. She gathered strawberries and wildflowers and new friends. Through her eyes I saw her friends as all near-genius writers and artists and thinkers. Because she loved them, she enlarged them and endowed them with amazing attributes.

I thought she had become a little dangerous. She was certainly eyebrow-raising! I worried that she had gone over some edge of her soul and had lost sight of her previous appropriate boundaries. When I expressed embarrassment to a friend about her public displays of affection with her new fiancé, I had to be reminded, "Valerie, just be glad she can feel these things at her age."

I was young, proper, and conventional. I was already poised for my Protestant nun stage when I would crepe my soul in browns, blacks, and navy blues. My mother, in contrast, was much younger than I. She was done with the dumpy, frumpy, dowdy, weighted-down forties approach to life; she had been there, done that. She was almost seventy, and her soul blazed with hot pinks and lemon yellows. This was not the wearing of purple and red just for the shock value. Her clothing appropriately reflected her joy, not her lack of social propriety. It was as if she had thrown out every youthful weight she had carried in her early years and was now squeezing all the joy she could from life. Every drop.

Victor Hugo said, "When grace is joined with wrinkles it is adorable." Adorable or not, I still worried about her. I worried if she would be able to handle physically her own hyperactive, live-to-the-max lifestyle. Her angina was so severe that I usually had to carry not only my own purse, diaper bag, et cetera, but her purse as well. And then what I feared happened. She suffered a massive heart attack at sixty-nine. I really think the joy factor was too much for her heart. The last pictures taken of her were of her laughing with tears running down her cheeks. I remember the evening so clearly. We had laughed so hard my jaws hurt the next day.

Then, suddenly, she died. She died dancing. Square dancing. She had just turned to her friends and said, "Oh, what fun!" Then she slumped over in her chair and bang! . . . she was gone.

Life was better at the end than it was at the beginning for my mother. I admire that. I think that I, too, would like to die dancing. Why not throw off the weights of early living and travel lighter as I age? I want to dress my soul more brightly—to rid myself of the dark, depressed, mourning clothes of my youth and wrap myself instead in the colors of fireworks. (I hope my children will not be too shocked!) When will I pick strawberries and wildflowers and endow my friends with so much love that they become people of high value to all who know them through me—when, if not now? Here's to many "mornings after" when my jaw hurts from laughing so hard the night before! Maybe I will manage to raise a few stodgy eyebrows and be thought of as somewhat dangerous. That would be great! Oh, that my ending would be better than my beginning! I intend to get better at this thing called living.

Don't you?

PART 4

Night Light

Prudence

DA BIG CHAIR

By Kim Bolton with Chris Wave

God will speak to this people, to whom he said, "This is
the resting place, let the weary rest"; and, "This is the
place of repose"—but they would not listen. So then, the
word of the LORD to them will become: Do and do, do
and do.

Isaiah 28:11–13

Jelly globs beckoned me to release them from their incarceration to
my table. I picked the path of least resistance across my kitchen
floor, hoping to avoid the toddler cookie-drool that threatened to
glue me in place. Unmade beds, dirty dishes, unopened bills, carpool
responsibilities, the needs of my family—what about my needs?

From the middle of the screaming piles, a small, sweet voice beckoned. I peered over the edge of the basket I was carrying—laundry
mounded past my eyebrows.

"Hey, Mom," he said. "Why dontcha come and sit wif me in da
big chair?"

Balancing my precarious load, I explained to my toddler, "I have
too much to do; I can't sit in the big chair or anywhere else, Honey."

"Come on, come and sit wight here by me." He patted the space between him and the arm rest.

"I can't, Baby," I moaned, thinking of the chores that numbered in the legion.

"Come on now; it'll just take a minute, just a wittle minute." He smiled the irresistible smile of a two-year-old boy. He continued to pat the waiting space next to him.

I dropped my load of laundry. I melted into the seat next to him. And he placed his tiny hand on my face and said, "Now, isn't dis nice, Mom?"

"Yes," I said, "it's wonderful." We sat together for ninety seconds.

Then as if he understood the demands waiting for me, he tenderly patted my leg and said, "You can go now."

Just like Jesus. He waits, patting the space next to him and says, "This is the resting place—next to me."

"Maybe tonight," we say, "maybeafterlunchmaybewhenItakeout-thetrashmaybetonightbeforebedmaybetomorrowafterschoolbeforebed." And it doesn't happen.

He keeps patting.

Jesus keeps patting the space between him and the "next thing," saying, "Just a little minute. A little minute in My Big Chair. It will change your day, probably your life."

"Maybebeforebathtime, bedtime, suppertimemaybemaybe," we drone.

Sit yourself in da big chair. Find your spot in the quiet place. Sit there, so that the Lord doesn't have to say to you, "O.K. then, 'do and do, do and do.'"

TREASURE IN THE TRASH

By Luci Swindoll

Tax time is usually a drag for most of us. But there are some years when, after April 15, we feel absolutely poverty-stricken. That's how I felt some years ago when my taxes were so high I had little left for the "frivolous" things of life: little luxuries like buying books, taking trips, eating out.

I put myself on a very strict budget for three months, making it a point to write down every cent I spent for even the most insignificant things, like toothpaste or a Coke. I canceled various magazines and newspapers to which I had subscriptions and thought of every way under the sun to cut costs around my house. Actually, if the truth be known, it was kinda fun.

About three weeks into this exacting self-imposed regimen I was praying one afternoon that God would give me a creative idea of how I could have a lot of fun on little money. As I was leaving the home of a friend that evening I noticed she was tossing out a mum plant simply because its blooms were wilting. I felt sorry for the plant and asked her if I could have it. Incredulously, she announced, "But it's dead." I assured her that given enough time, I could revive it. She doubted that . . . which was the only challenge I needed to go full tilt on a new project. This was the answer to my prayer. I was going to create a garden, and it wasn't going to cost me a penny.

I was living in a complex where people would often toss their old dead (or dying) house plants in the garbage bins, with no further thought. I began to collect everybody's discarded mum plants. Some had been cut back, but most were just lying there with brown leaves, looking like there was no life left in them. In the course of the next three or four days I must have brought home more than twenty plants in various throes of death rattle, and nursed them back to health.

First, I cut them all back, watered them, and placed them on the upper deck just outside my bedroom window. I sang to them and played Mozart for them. When necessary, I killed aphids with a concoction of rubbing alcohol, Murphy's Oil Soap, and water. I had become Martha Stewart. My friends accused me of making my own dirt.

I fertilized those precious little plants faithfully. In short, I loved them into blooming again. And did they bloom! I started taking pictures of them at various stages of growth: with small buds, buds just breaking into blossoms, fully blooming, and finally dying back. At one point, I'll bet I counted seven or eight hundred blooms. Magnificent hues of every color of mum in the world: yellow, orange, white, purple, rust, brown, mauve . . . they were gorgeous! And when people walked by or went outside, they looked up at that array of color. Some pointed, others took pictures, and everybody commented about my flower garden.

My friends who had teased me unmercifully about collecting dead plants began asking for their plants back. They begged me for mums. "Please, Luci, just enough for the table for my dinner party?" No way! Every time I looked at those sweet flowers I was reminded of God's brilliant answer to my prayer.

Have you been down in the mouth lately? Want to do something fun or uplifting for your spirit, but find yourself with no money to splurge? Ask God for a creative idea. He will give you one, and you will experience a dimension of his giving that is different from the rest. It will be restorative to your soul, because it will once again prove his ability to provide for you, even in odd, zany, off-the-wall ways.

Excuse me . . . I'd like to sit here and chat longer, but it's garbage day so I think I'll go see if I can find a few dead plants.

HIGH AND HOLY WORK

By Amy Imbody

The end of the day. A hot cup of tea. Every child tucked in, and I sit at the computer at last. Time to write! Time for the brain work! The poems! The essays! The novel!

I type the first title. I try not to notice the slight motion behind me. Quickly I type the magnificent line of poetry that came to me during a stoplight this morning. I try not to notice the sound of small feet. I try to ignore my peripheral vision. There is no boy.

But of course, there is.

I turn my head slowly, looking quite fierce. Wide blue eyes stare guilelessly at me. I try to look very stern. In fact, I feel extremely cross.

"Mommy, will you read to me?" A pause, then quickly, " From the Bible?"

Oh, no! I am undone! Could I possibly scream at him, "NO, I WILL NOT READ TO YOU FROM THE BIBLE!!" (Lord, set a guard over my lips, that I might not sin against Thee!)

Up the stairs together we go. I droop a little, but I go. I read a psalm. I rub his back. I sing a lullaby. There is no doubt in my mind that had I stayed at the computer, the only result would have been wood, hay, and stubble. Sand in my mouth. Chasing after wind.

Because here is my high and holy work: at the bed of my child, who cannot sleep. God forgive me the arrogance that dares to assume that my brain is holier than my hands, the world more important than this small disciple.

A Hairy Story

By Liz Curtis Higgs

I personally wouldn't let my dear Bill anywhere near my hair. The truth is, the woman I pay to hold the scissors sometimes gives me pause. Oh, there were a few days back in 1988 when I thought we'd really hit on something, but the rest of the time it's too long, too short, too curly, too flat, too red, too blonde, or decidedly too gray—though that last one is not my stylist's fault.

As for the cutting and styling itself, that's where I do depend on Carol. I've known her longer than I've known my husband. Our paths crossed in 1984, and I've faithfully sat in her chair ever since. When Carol switched salons, I followed her across town.

"Whither thou goest, I will go," I assured her.

Who wouldn't declare lifelong loyalty to someone who combines amateur therapy skills with the latest techniques in blunt cutting?

Carol listened patiently through my career and dating woes, nodding sympathetically as her scissors snipped away. Those were the perm years—natural color, unnatural curl. Then when hubby-to-be Bill came into my life, Carol and I dumped the perm in favor of longer locks to please my sweetie.

What is it with men and long hair?

Months later, it was Carol who styled the tresses of my wedding party, and Carol again who gave me a pedicure the week before my first child was slated to arrive, so I'd have fashionable toes in the delivery room.

Talk about a labor of love!

Our relationship isn't one-sided, either. I sang at Carol's wedding and rejoiced when she began taking college courses at night. We've laughed, cried, and compared notes on husbands, kids, and cleaning services. You can't simply walk away from that kind of dual commitment over something as frivolous as a few frizzy perms or doubtful dye jobs.

Besides, the mere thought of trying a new stylist gives me the willies. Make that will-he's. As in, "Will he understand about my sparse spots?" or "Will she know how to tame that strange cowlick in the back?" Someone else might do a better job, but then again, what if it's worse? What if my hair comes out five different lengths and three different colors?

Hey, it can happen. Carol once had to rescue a poor high school senior who'd dyed his hair purple to match his prom tux. He spent five hours (and untold dollars) in her chair while she corrected another stylist's nightmare-in-violet creation.

But he probably never darkened her chair again. Men are fickle when it comes to hair. Any five-dollar barber will do. The way my Bill sees it, why bother making an appointment with a pricey stylist when he can drop in Buck's Barber Shop unannounced, thumb through a few issues of *Field & Stream,* plunk down a ten, and leave with change and short hair?

"But what do you and Buck talk about?" I once asked him.

He wrinkled his brow in confusion. "I dunno. The weather? Reds baseball, maybe?" Bill sighed. "Look, the whole thing takes ten minutes, tops."

Aha! There's the difference. Women spend a minimum of forty-five minutes in a salon; two hours with color; three hours for a perm with a manicure. Toss in a facial or a wax job, and we're approaching half a day with our smocked sister.

We spend more money with them too. Lots more money. Bill was aghast the first time he saw a credit-card receipt from a visit with

Carol. "Sixty dollars?!? You look the same as you did this morning. Can't you find someone less expensive?"

Less expensive, sure. But that's not the point. Carol and I are friends. Girl buddies. Partners in the fight against dark roots and stray chin hairs. She's seen me in no makeup. No clothes, for that matter, stretched out on a massage table wearing nothing but a towel and a smile.

Who could say sayonara to a soul sister like that?

One January, however, I came frighteningly close to committing hair-care infidelity. Just the memory of it makes my scalp itch. I was facing a photo session for a local magazine cover, and arrangements were made for Jacobson's to do my makeup and hair. After the cosmetician did a bang-up job on eyes, lips, and cheeks, it was time to put my thinning hair in the hands of a stranger named Steve.

Steve the Stylist rested his hands lightly on my shoulders, and my stomach tightened. I felt like a nervous teenager on a first date.

"Is there a particular way you'd like me to style your hair?"

Yes, I wanted to say. Carol's way! Instead, I gulped. "Nooo, just make me look ten pounds thinner and I'll be happy."

His graceful hands danced around my head, comb in one hand, industrial-strength hair spray in the other. I watched in amazement. I was getting thinner!

Gee, Carol never parted it like that. How did he do that lift-and-poof thing on the side? Fascinating.

Steve finally whipped off my plastic cape with a flourish. "There you are, Liz. What do you think?"

I think I'm in love. No, no, not with you, just your hands. Are you this good with scissors? Know your way around a bottle of peroxide? I realized the dangerous path my imagination was taking me down and mentally swatted away the little voices saying, "He's the one! He's the one! Leave Carol and cleave to Steve!"

When he slipped me his card and suggested I give him a call sometime, I stuffed it in my pocket, mumbled a red-faced "thank you," and hotfooted it for the door.

Whew! That was close. I'd resisted temptation, but barely. How could I even think of breaking up a friendship that was in its second decade, just for the thrill of a zippy new do? Sure, Steve might have some fresh ideas for my stale tresses, but what would I say when I saw Carol at the grocery store after being absent from her chair for six months and sporting a new color or cut? Even without a big red A on my chest, she would know: I'd been unfaithful.

I knew I should have tossed Steve's business card in the circular file, but I couldn't resist tucking it in my Rolodex, "just in case." In case Carol moved away or quit the business. Or was eaten by sharks. Otherwise, I would not defect to Steve. Would not, could not.

But my fingers kept flipping past his name. Hmm. Would Carol notice if I did one little color weave with Steve? Maybe a teensy trim, between real haircuts? If I timed it right, she'd never be the wiser. I reached for the phone and dialed Steve's salon.

The receptionist was sharp, cool, professional. Yes, Steve had an opening on Tuesday. A trim? Of course, no problem, 2:00 is fine. See you then, Mrs. Higgs.

I almost slammed the phone down. What was I thinking?

As the calendar marched toward Tuesday, I spent more time on my hair than usual, trying to convince myself to undo our risk-filled liaison. It's not that bad a cut, I told myself. In fact, it's a very good cut, or Steve couldn't have styled it so nicely.

Tuesday morning dawned gray and menacing. Cowardice leaped from my heart and into my fingers as I dialed the Other Salon's number and canceled my appointment, muttering a feeble excuse about my too-full schedule.

I waited for my racing heart to slow back down to normal and then hit the speed-dialing button that instantly put me in touch with my regular salon. My salon, Carol's salon. Home.

"A cut with Carol at 2:00 o'clock? No problem, Liz. See you then. Hug the kids for me."

Ahh. I hung up the phone in blessed relief, silently slipping Steve's card in the wastebasket. No more flirting with temptation; I'd stick with a place where everybody knows my name.

Especially Carol, the one woman who can (almost) guarantee me a good hair day.

HOLIDAY MEMORIES

By Dale Hanson Bourke

A friend of mine and I were discussing the importance of holiday traditions recently. Both new to the art of mothering, we were suddenly feeling the pressure to establish traditions for our families "before it was too late." After all, we both had young sons who, we were told, needed meaningful holidays as much as they needed play groups, snug-fitting diapers, and educational toys. Who knew what would happen to our toddlers if we didn't provide the right environment? Would they be ostracized in grade school? Would they grow up and confess to psychological abuse in their formative years?

As the holidays approached, I began taking this task quite seriously—reading books, studying expert advice, listening to "successful" mothers—when it suddenly occurred to me that my own holidays had been nearly traditionless.

To say my family *always* did things one way would be to deny the essentially spontaneous nature of the Hansons. We never let one celebration serve as precedent for the next. We rarely followed a path we'd walked before. In fact, my memories of holidays are a crazy quilt of sights, sounds, and activities—few tied to one another.

There was the Thanksgiving that we were in the midst of moving and my mother served a turkey roll in the center of her large, hand painted platter. Sitting among the boxes, we laughed until we cried at the sight of the pitiful little processed bird. And there was the year we had our Thanksgiving lunch at a hot dog stand so that we could travel to both grandparents' houses in one day and keep peace among the relatives.

There was the Christmas that my parents let me open "just one gift" on Christmas Eve. Knowing my essentially greedy nature, they counted on my choosing the largest box, which they had filled with nuts. Although we had a good laugh, they sensed my disappointment, and let me open the rest of my presents that night.

And then there was the Christmas morning that the presents arrived in the shower stall. We had no fireplace, so my father explained, with an almost straight face, that Santa must have lost weight and squeezed through the faucet to deliver the gifts.

I suppose, after reviewing my memories, that there was one holiday tradition in my family. The tradition was humor, and it had a way of wrapping itself around all the diverse activities of holidays and other times of the year. It got us through turkey rolls and hot dogs, unexpected presents, and houses without fireplaces. It made our Christmas tree sparkle and gave us moments of joy when we least expected them.

It salved the wounds of childhood, too, and eased me though skinned knees, the deaths of pets, and the disappointments of friendships. It put sibling rivalries in perspective and gave me confidence that I belonged.

If there was one thing we were always able to do, it was to laugh at ourselves and even at each other. Sometimes one of us took it personally and had to be lovingly teased back into the fold, but mostly we all knew that no matter what, we were part of one crazy, loving family. Even if we celebrated holidays erratically or treated tradition irreverently, we still knew that family times were special.

So as I prepare my own young family for the holidays, I'm becoming more relaxed about establishing traditions. My son can probably enjoy the holidays without a special menu, a keepsake ornament, or a carefully trimmed tree. But I don't think he can truly appreciate any holiday without love and humor.

Our Mess is Growing on Me

By Joyce Maynard

Don't ask my why, with all three of my children due to celebrate their birthdays in the next four weeks, I'd feel compelled to suggest to my son Charlie that we hold a Valentine-making party. But that's what I did last week. And then, of course, Willy wanted to ask one or two of his friends to join the crowd, and Charlie wanted to invite a couple of his guests to sleep over after the party. Then one or two of the others got wind of the sleepover plan. And before you could say "tension headache" there were ten children trooping into our house after school on a Friday afternoon, carrying paper doilies, scissors, glitter, sleeping bags, toothbrushes and stuffed animals. "You must be crazy," said one of the mothers, as she dropped off her son. "You're going to have one terrible mess to clean up tomorrow."

In preparation for this event I'd covered our dining room table with newspaper and set out a vast array of craft supplies: ribbon, lace, construction paper, glue, sequins, buttons, stickers, and a box full of old postcards and catalogues to cut up. Somewhere along the line (but not in a cemetery) I'd acquired a huge boxful of plastic flowers, which seemed ideal for gluing onto valentines, along with wallpaper samples and gold paper and pieces of old costume jewelry. Our local video store had been clearing out used video cassette boxes at a quarter apiece, so I'd laid in a supply of those, figuring they'd make great three dimensional valentines, to put treasures in. And they did.

By four o'clock our house was a mess. Popcorn popping, paper scraps covering the floor, glitter everywhere. But the funny thing was that though our house was a wreck, the valentines were beautiful, and the children—far from having lost control—were as focused and concentrated and harmonious a group as I can remember seeing at our house in all our years of hosting large gatherings of kids. In fact, I'd say, there almost seemed to be a correlation between the chaos on my dining room table and floor and the calm amongst the children. I actually left the room after a while, to pour myself a cup of coffee and read the paper, because everyone was so busy at work they didn't need me.

Around dinner time, as the valentine making slowed down, I ordered a giant pizza and set out plates and cups. Gradually the kids filtered downstairs to our playroom for ping pong and a movie. My original plan had been to spend that time clearing away the valentine mess and getting our house back in order. But I decided instead to snuggle up with the kids and watch the movie, too.

Sometime close to eleven, when I tucked the children in, I confronted the mess in my dining room again. Would I clean it up? No.

The next morning, when I got up and came downstairs, one or two of Charlie's friends were back at work, making valentines. Gradually, throughout the morning, others filtered in and out of the room, taking turns with the glue gun and the stapler, the wallpaper books and the tape. Parents began swinging by to pick up their kids. By noon the population at our house was back down to the usual number.

But only briefly. Another batch of friends were due at our house for dinner that night—mostly grown-ups this time, plus a few of their children. There was a time when that fact would have meant I'd be spending my afternoon cleaning. But it was a glorious day, and I longed to go bike riding with my kids. So when Audrey suggested we leave our craft supplies out and make dinner a buffet in the living room, I didn't argue.

In the end, a lot of the adults who turned up that night ended up making valentines. And as for me—instead of scrambling frantically to make everything orderly, I knew order was an impossible goal and chose instead to do something I don't always manage at my own parties: I sat down and visited with my friends. Nobody seemed to think less of me for the bits of paper and rickrack on my floor.

Well, that was a week ago, and the mess in our dining room is with us still. Hardly a day goes by that someone—paper boy, neighbor or friend—doesn't end up sitting down and making something at the table. One whole wall of the room is covered with their creations. Now my daughter has even put up a sign that says "Gallery."

The thing about a giant mess is, once it's there it can't get much worse. The other great thing about a mess is that when you have one already, you don't have to worry about making one. And as long as you leave a mess, you don't get mad at your children for not cleaning it up. You don't get tense when a toddler walks in with her hands full of those little candy hearts that say things like "Oh, You Kid." Which means the toddler's mother doesn't get tense either. So what if candy hearts end up all over the floor?

Every day I walk through my dining room and ask myself: Is this the day we clean up the mess? And every day I conclude, no, not quite yet. Imagine, I think to myself: If I had vacuumed and dusted that first day, the dining room would already be due for vacuuming again. As it is, instead of spending all that time vacuuming, I've spent it making things. Valentine cards. Birthday cards. Cards that celebrate no special occasion whatsoever, besides the simple joy of being alive.

I have no doubt my children will find plenty of things to criticize me for, over the years. But something tells me, twenty years from now, not a one of them will be lying on some therapist's couch, complaining that their mother didn't spend enough time vacuuming up glitter. More likely they'll talk about all the times I yelled at them to pick up their messes.

"This was a happy week," my daughter said to me the other day. "Oh yes?" I said to her. "Why is that?" "I don't exactly know," she said. "But I love our mess." I knew what she meant. Our mess is growing on me too, in more ways than one.

KNOWING WHEN TO UNLOAD

By Jill Briscoe

I gasped, "I'm sinking."

"I know," my husband said.

"I've signed all these book contracts—"

"Why?" he interrupted.

"Because—"

"Because you can't say no," Stuart said.

"Well, that's part of it."

"You've overloaded yourself again," he pointed out. "And don't blame other people," he added. "You did it to yourself."

He was right.

I thought of Jesus saying to His disciples, "Come to me, all you who are weary and burdened, and I will give you rest" (Matthew 11:28).

That word "burdened," incidentally, was used only one other place in the Bible, when Paul was in a storm at sea and the sailors had to lighten the over-burdened ship. They threw the cargo overboard in an attempt to save everyone.

Now as I was sinking, I thought how wonderful that picture in Matthew was: Jesus talking to 12 men, many fishermen who knew well enough what would happen if their boats were overloaded. Twice Jesus told them to throw their nets over the side of the ship in a particular place and they caught so many fish their nets began to break. The Lord's lesson was clear: Yoked to Him, tied closely to His big boat, their small vessels would have the help needed to bear the loads He asked them to carry. Their burden could even seem light.

I knew I would need to figure what sort of a boat I am. How am I crafted? Am I a cargo ship, tug boat, a submarine doing all my work out of sight, a skiff, a battleship, the Titanic?

I thought back to when I was a child. My father, home on leave from World War II, took my sister and me to the Liverpool dockyards near our home. He wanted us to see the merchant ships that brought us food.

"Brave men have risked their lives to bring us this precious cargo," he told us.

I noticed a line painted around the center of each vessel. "What's that for?" I asked.

"To show the people loading up the ship how much it's made to carry," he said. "If they put too much on, the line disappears. The boat will sink. If they put too little inside, it won't be full enough to do what it was made to do. Each boat is made by its builder to carry just the right amount."

God, I think, has made me a large cargo ship. I carry a lot, but there is still a level I need to watch. If I'm not taking anything on for Him I will feel strangely light and unfulfilled. If, however, I say yes to every invitation to speak, write, serve and help, I'll soon be at the bottom of the sea.

Like boats at the dock, I realize, we are all different. I have a friend who is a little skiff. Whenever I get low in the water she tells me a funny story or takes me to lunch, lightening my load by helping me relax. But it usually takes all she has to cheer me. After her encouragement, she's done for the day. That's how God made her. It would be ridiculous for me to load some of my projects on her boat.

When I allowed other people to pile a cargo of books into my hold, my husband decided to inspect the ship. He took an inventory and struck off two of the six book projects.

"But, Stuart," I wailed.

"Whoa," he said, laughing. "I'll get you out of these two things. We'll get the publishers to store the books on the dock for a future journey when you're not carrying so much." And that's what we did.

God, I must remind myself, is the boat builder. He knows who we are, how big our holds are, what He wants us to carry. The way to fulfillment lies in keeping the painted line on our ships above the water line and to keep sailing.

SPRINKLES OF GRACE

By Carol Kuykendall

Before I became a mom, I imagined that mothering would bring out the best in me. I'd take charge and be in complete control of my time, my emotions and my children. I'd make the right decisions and then simply carry them out. Head over heart. Mind over matter. After all, that's what moms are supposed to do.

What was I thinking?

After becoming a mom, of course I learned that I don't always do the right thing, even when I know what the right thing is. But I like to think that's when God sprinkles me—and my children—with his grace. Take this example.

Late one afternoon, while grocery shopping with both a toddler and a preschooler stuffed into my cart (the same two children who had been pushing me to my limits all day long), I totally lost my ability to think rationally. They were whining about being hungry. I was hungry. We were all tired. They wanted cookies. I have to admit, I wanted cookies too. More than cookies, I wanted peace. No whining.

"Please, Mommy, please, Mommy. Mommy! Cookies. We want cookies."

Everything in my head logically told me, *You don't give children cookies just because they whine for cookies. You don't give children cookies an hour before dinner. Saying "No!" to cookies builds character in children and teaches them about delayed gratification and reinforces the fact that you—the mother—are in control here.*

"Please, Mommy. I need a cookie! Cookie!" they said in unison, pointing to a package on the shelf in the long (*very* long) cookie aisle.

Something inside me snapped. I don't know exactly what. But I do remember grabbing the package of cookies off the shelf, ripping it open, and then handing some cookies to the two children in my cart. I even ate a couple myself.

It didn't make sense, but it made silence, and at that moment, I wanted silence more than sense, even though the decision went against everything I knew in my head.

Later I felt a twinge of guilt when the checker lifted the half-empty package of cookies out of my cart and grinned at my two cookie monsters who still had sticky crumbs smeared across their faces.

"It's okay," she said as she ran the package across her scanner. "I'm a mom too."

Though we were total strangers, she and I shared an intimate moment of understanding that moms sometimes do what works instead of what's right. As I wheeled my cart out of the store, filled with groceries and two contented children, I couldn't help but think that God understands these mom moments too, and cuts us some slack as he sprinkles us with his grace.

A Mammoth Memory

By Gwendolyn Mitchell Diaz

Mrs. Uncapher's third grade class was given an assignment. They were to make a dinosaur replica to go along with a written report, and Jonathan was assigned the Tyrannosaurus Rex, "King of the Tyrant Lizards!"

"Oh boy!" I exclaimed with more sarcasm than enthusiasm. "How are you going to do that? I guess you could make a shadow box, or maybe a clay model. How about a special drawing with salt and yarn glued on top to give it some neat texture?"

"Nope!"

Jonathan immediately informed me that none of the above would do. He wanted to make a papier-mâché dinosaur, just like the one he had seen at the museum, a GREAT BIG dinosaur that would stand up all by itself and look real!

Through the years, our family has completed a great many art projects, and we have a huge closet devoted to craft supplies. However, none of us had ever worked with papier-mâché. I tried to relay this lack of expertise and the problems it might engender to my son, but he was insistent.

"Don't do it!" one of my friends advised me. "It's just not worth the time or effort. So what if he gets a C. Go buy him some play dough. No dinosaur is worth more than ten minutes of your time!"

TIME—that was the real issue here. Did I want to invest the time to help my son make a papier-mâché dinosaur when he could get by with something much less time-consuming?

As I looked at the youngest of my four sons in his hand-me-down shirt, broken-off shoelaces, and his brother's favorite baseball cap, I decided that he needed not only my time, but also the attention that went with it. We scrounged through three craft stores before we found instructions on how to work with papier-mâché. Hours later, after dipping thousands of strips of newspaper into gallons of watery glue and spreading them across an over-sized balloon, our project began to take shape—a round shape—unlike any dinosaur I had ever seen! But it was a start.

Paper towel tubes and hanger wires covered with masking tape became legs and tiny arms. A huge, long tail was added to the spherical body. We fashioned an egg-shaped head on top, and voilá, about five hours into the project we had a . . . well, dinosaur.

Actually, it didn't resemble a dinosaur at all. So we quickly experimented on how to make paper pulp, and by globbing it in various places our project took on a more "dinosaurial" form. That took about two more days.

Altogether our dinosaur project encompassed three days of our lives. In the end, Jonathan was happy. He loved his dinosaur. And I loved the special time we spent together. We talked and laughed. I learned all kinds of third grade jokes and secrets and a whole lot about my eight-year-old son. He learned a lot about the "olden days" (back when I was growing up). Best of all, we talked about wonderful biblical truths, like God created everything—things as little as ants and as big as dinosaurs—and God knows EVERYTHING you do, EVERYWHERE you are—even when you're hiding under the covers!

Based on my experience, whoever tried to sell us working moms on the idea that when it comes to raising kids the "quality" of time spent is more important than the "quantity" of time had it all wrong.

I am more convinced than ever that true quality times can only grow out of quantities of time . . . time spent just being together.

Jonathan and I didn't just make a dinosaur that week. We made a mammoth memory!

STRAWBERRIES AND CREAM

A Lesson in Diplomacy

By Karen Dona Stuart

Rays of morning sunshine warmed us as Mother and I stooped to pick the first strawberries of summer. The walled French garden must have seemed a tranquil place amidst the rubble in the countryside, evidence still of the war just past.

It was June 1955. We lived on the "economy" in a rented cottage near Bordeaux—a young military family: my American father, my English mother, and me.

As we brought our basket of strawberries to the pump and rinsed them off, Mother urged me to run down the lane and invite the village children to come up for strawberries and cream. We had been fortunate to have purchased a liter of cream from the farmer who owned the small cottage we rented.

I must have spoken passable French; or perhaps not, as children never really need words to communicate with one another. My friends all came: Étienne, Marie, Margaux, and Claire. Hands scrubbed clean, we pulled wobbly stools up to the rustic wooden table. Mother filled small bowls heaping with strawberries, then ladled on sugar. Eyes got wide. Sugar was a luxury seldom known to the children of this poor hamlet. And cream, butter, milk, and eggs were always reserved for the American soldiers who had money to spend.

With timid anticipation, our guests accepted the bowls in front of them. Mother picked up the pitcher of cream and passed it to Étienne. She smiled. He smiled. He looked at us askance, then slowly lifted the pitcher to his lips and took a long drink. He passed it to Marie, who did the same, and on around the table. As it reached me, Mother took the pitcher before I could pour the cream onto my strawberries, as I knew I should have properly done. Mother smiled. She picked up the pitcher, put it to her lips, and drank; then she passed it on to me to do the same. I learned of diplomacy that day: The cultural ambassador in our family had given me my first lesson. I was four.

KELLIE, MY MAIDEN WARRIOR

By Patsy Y. Iwasaki

My family has a history of girls. My mother had two sisters, I have a sister, my older sister has two daughters and I have a four-year-old daughter. So in essence, we've got the girl thing down real good.

My sister and I grew up wearing matching outfits complete with coordinating shoes, socks and hair accessories. Both her daughters love to take dance classes, play "princess" and wear pretty dresses.

So when I gave birth to my daughter Kellie in 1995, the whole family rejoiced because we all just adored little girls. Although I was in pain from an emergency cesarean section and Kellie was a month premature, when I took home my tiny, 3-pound, 14-ounce girl from the hospital, visions began to dance in my head: matching mother-daughter dresses, elaborate hairstyles, tea parties, fingernail painting sessions—my dreams went on and on.

When I wasn't going insane from lack of sleep, trying to get a handle on breastfeeding and the other joys and pains of being a new mother, I had a blast during the first six months. On my energetic days, I'd clothe my little one in all of the beautiful outfits given by kind family and friends. I'd even clip what little hair she had with cute hair clips which my husband promptly called "whalespouts."

But sometime during the second half of her first year of life, Kellie began exercising the use of her own hands. She learned that she could reach up and pull off those annoying hair things that Mommy loved to put on, uprooting almost all the hair she had! She started getting little bald spots and I had to stop my "doll dressing" sessions.

As she got older, she would fuss and cry when I put her in dresses. I knew I had to choose my battles carefully and this wasn't worth it, so Kellie began wearing T-shirts and shorts, albeit decorative, cute shirts.

When she started talking after turning one, my daughter would simply say "No" when I began pulling out a frilly dress for Sunday church service for her to wear. She'd toddle over to the pile of shirts and wave one at me.

"Please, please, Kellie," I'd say, pleading with her. Sometimes she'd relent and sometimes she wouldn't.

At about the same time, she began to show great interest in bugs, insects and my husband's tools. Since we live in Hawaii where there's an abundance of creepy, crawly things, there was no lack of resources for scientific investigation. My little girl began to grab chameleons, geckos and skinks with surprising skill and adeptness.

My mother continued to give gifts of Barbie dolls, stuffed animals and even a small dollhouse, saying, "She needs to have more girl things." But God was already working on my heart, bringing to mind the scene in the gospel of Mark where the children were brought to Jesus to be blessed. The disciples were upset and rebuked them, but Jesus said, "Permit the children to come to Me; do not hinder them; for the kingdom of God belongs to such as these" (Mark 10:14).

If Jesus accepted the children just as they were and encouraged us to be like children to receive the Kingdom of God, then what was I doing, trying to mold my child into something she was not? Obviously, despite the family's girl gene pool, Kellie had been given a splash of tomboy spirit. I realized I needed to appreciate her for who she was and as my husband said, "Her feminine side will come around."

I purchased a bug kit and accepted the fact that we'd always have extra residents in and around the house—as long as they stayed in the bug box! I began to see the value of her personality. Whereas I scream and get a long-handled broom to attack unwanted pests, Kellie calmly grabs a stray gecko in the house. In this day and age, her interest in mechanics and tools will eventually help her fix the car, paint the fence and fix the sink disposal. Useful abilities that I wish I had. Last Christmas we gave her a "Tim Allen" (*Home Improvement* TV show) child's tool belt with real, smaller-sized working tools. After she opened it, she immediately put it on, stopped opening the rest of her presents, and announced, "I want to go pound nails now."

Although Kellie is still a T-shirt-and-shorts kind of girl, often pretending to be a pirate wielding a sword or an Indian shooting a bow and arrows, she also takes time to paint her fingernails with Mommy. Like her name Kellie, which means "maiden warrior," and her Japanese middle name "Kaori," which means "sweet fragrance," it's a good balance.

Even Grandma has come around. For an Easter gift to her youngest granddaughter, my mother gave Kellie a miniature "Ken" doll tool set.

PART 5

Whistling in the Dark
Courage

PREGNANT IN NEW YORK

By Anna Quindlen

I have two enduring memories of the hours just before I gave birth to my first child. One is of finding a legal parking space on Seventy-eighth Street between Lexington and Park, which made my husband and me believe that we were going inside the hospital to have a child who would always lead a charmed life. The other is of walking down Lexington Avenue, stopping every couple of steps to find myself a visual focal point—a stop sign, a red light, a pair of $200 shoes in a store window—and doing what the Lamaze books call first-stage breathing. It was 3:00 a.m. and coming toward me through a magenta haze of what the Lamaze books call discomfort were a couple in evening clothes whose eyes were popping out of their perfect faces. "Wow," said the man when I was at least two steps past them. "She looks like she's ready to burst."

I love New York, but it's a tough place to be pregnant. It's a great place for half sour pickles, chopped liver, millionaires, actors, dancers, Akita dogs, nice leather goods, fur coats, and baseball, but it is a difficult place to have any kind of disability and, as anyone who has filled out the forms for a maternity leave lately will tell you, pregnancy is considered a disability. There's no privacy in New York;

everyone is right up against everyone else and they all feel compelled to say what they think. When you look like a hot-air balloon with insufficient ballast, that's not good.

New York has no pity: it's every man for himself, and since you are yourself-and-a-half, you fall behind. There's a rumor afoot that if you are pregnant you can get a seat on the A train at rush hour, but it's totally false. There are, in fact, parts of the world in which pregnancy can get you a seat on public transportation, but none of them are within the boundaries of the City—with the possible exception of some unreconstructed parts of Staten Island.

What you get instead are rude comments, unwarranted intrusions and deli countermen. It is a little-known fact that New York deli countermen can predict the sex of an unborn child. (This is providing that you order, of course. For a counterman to provide this service requires a minimum order of seventy-five cents.) This is how it works: You walk into a deli and say, "Large fruit salad, turkey on rye with Russian, a large Perrier and a tea with lemon." The deli counterman says, "Who you buying for, the Rangers?" and all the other deli countermen laugh.

This is where many pregnant women make their mistake. If it is wintertime and you are wearing a loose coat, the preferred answer to this question is, "I'm buying for all the women in my office." If it is summer and you are visibly pregnant, you are sunk. The deli counterman will lean over the counter and say, studying your contours, "It's a boy." He will then tell a tedious story about sex determination, his Aunt Olga, and a clove of garlic, while behind you people waiting in line shift and sigh and begin to make Zero Population Growth and fat people comments. (I once dealt with an East Side counterman who argued with me about the tea because he said it was bad for the baby, but he was an actor waiting for his big break, not a professional.) Deli countermen do not believe in amniocentesis. Friends who have had amniocentesis tell me that once or twice they tried to argue: "I already know it's a girl." "You are wrong." They gave up: "Don't forget the napkins."

There are also cabdrivers. One promptly pulled over in the middle of Central Park when I told him I had that queasy feeling. When

I turned to get back into the cab, it was gone. The driver had taken the $1.80 on the meter as a loss. Luckily, I never had this problem again, because as I grew larger, nine out of ten cabdrivers refused to pick me up. They had read the tabloids. They knew about all those babies christened Checker (actually, I suppose now most of them are Plymouths) because they're born in the back seat in the Midtown Tunnel. The only way I could get a cabdriver to pick me up after the sixth month was to hide my stomach by having a friend walk in front of me. The exception was a really tiresome young cabdriver whose wife's due date was a week after mine and who wanted to practice panting with me for that evening's childbirth class. Most of the time I wound up taking public transportation.

And so it came down to the subways: men looking at their feet, reading their newspapers, working hard to keep from noticing me. One day on the IRT I was sitting down—it was a spot left unoccupied because the rainwater had spilled in the window from an elevated station—when I noticed a woman standing who was or should have been on her way to the hospital.

"When are you due?" I asked her. "Thursday," she gasped. "I'm September," I said. "Take my seat." She slumped down and said, with feeling, "You are the first person to give me a seat on the subway since I've been pregnant." Being New Yorkers, with no sense of personal privacy, we began to exchange subway, taxi, and deli counterman stories. When a man sitting nearby got up to leave, he snarled, "You wanted women's lib, now you got it."

Well, I'm here to say that I did get women's lib, and it is my only fond memory of being pregnant in New York. (Actually, I did find pregnancy useful on opening day at Yankee Stadium, when great swarms of people parted at the sight of me as though I were Charlton Heston in *The Ten Commandments*. But it had a pariah quality that was not totally soothing.)

One evening rush hour during my eighth month I was waiting for a train at Columbus Circle. The loudspeaker was crackling unintelligibly and ominously and there were as many people on the platform as currently live in Santa Barbara, California. Suddenly I had the dreadful feeling that I was being surrounded. "To get mugged at a time like this," I thought ruefully. "And this being New York, they'll probably try to take the baby, too." But as I looked around I saw that the people surrounding me were four women, some armed with shoulder bags. "You need protection," one said, and being New Yorkers, they ignored the fact that they did not know one another and joined forces to form a kind of phalanx around me, not unlike those that offensive linemen build around a quarterback.

When the train arrived and the doors opened, they moved forward, with purpose, and I was swept inside, not the least bit bruised. "Looks like a boy," said one with a grin, and as the train began to move, we all grabbed the silver overhead handles and turned away from one another.

THE MAGIC SOUND OF POETRY

By Christopher de Vinck

I was invited to speak at a small local press club on why reading has declined in the United States. After the introductions, I spoke briefly about the American culture and how it seems that we, as a people, are prone to avoiding the least amount of substance in the written word; we no longer want to exert anything more beyond the mere impulse of a sensation felt from watching events on television or on a movie screen. It is easier to watch lovers kiss than to admit that we are lonely and seek solace.

I concluded my talk by comparing poetry to a crow in winter. There was this crow that accompanied me one winter morning following a formidable snowstorm. As I began to shovel the driveway, I heard a loud cawing. I looked up and saw this bird looking down at me.

A man with a shovel in winter is as congruent as a crow sitting in a tree. But, I told the audience, place the man in the tree, or hand the crow the shovel, and then you have the possibility for poetry. If you have the crow recite a favorite tale, or if you tell the man to remember how it feels to be a crow, you might hear a magic sound.

I concluded the evening's talk by saying how sad it must be for people who do not read, for they miss hearing the magic sound, and then I read aloud a few selections from my own work. The people politely applauded, and, following a poorly attended reception, I was out in the dark on the street, walking alone toward my car.

"Mr. De Vinck!" someone called. "Mr. De Vinck, could I speak with you for a moment?"

I turned and saw through the dim lights of a distant building an old woman approaching. She extended her hand. It was warm and small.

"My name is Laura Denisovich. Denisovich like in the Solzhenitsyn book. Do you remember?"

"Yes, I remember the book."

"I read about your talk in the local paper, so I came." Laura Denisovich spoke with a Russian accent. "I wish to tell you something."

The street was draped in sheets of snow; trees like old men in drooping beards; bushes in the shape of plump, white loaves fresh from the oven; lawns filled with pillows and pancakes of snow. There was no wind.

"My grandmother, she liked to read."

I wasn't at first aware that the woman was simply following up on the lecture, for I was distracted by her face: Her right cheek was shriveled and distorted; otherwise, she was beautiful.

"When the czar was murdered, the people in my grandmother's village were told they were forbidden to read or possess books. My grandfather, he was quick to obey and began burning all the family books in the fireplace, but my grandmother, she hid Pushkin. You know Pushkin?"

I nodded yes.

"She kept his book under a loose step outside beside the porch. When my grandfather traveled on business, my grandmother would sit on the step and read aloud Pushkin's poems:

Always contented with his life
And with his dinner, and his wife.

I stood in the middle of a New Jersey winter, listening to old Laura Denisovich recite poetry.

Habit is heaven's own redress:
It takes the place of happiness.

"That is from his Eugene Onegin dedication poem," I said, and Laura nodded.

"It was my grandmother's most favorite poem. And when it was my time for me to learn how to read, it was from that book where I learned the shapes and sounds of the letters. They taught me how to read, my grandmother and Pushkin. I wanted to tell you this thing. And when you spoke about the crow, I was reminded of more lines my grandmother loved so well. I hadn't thought of such things for a long time until tonight:

Loved passed, the muse appeared, the weather
Of mind got clarity newfound;
Now free, I once more weave together
Emotion, thought, and magic sound.

"Do you see, Mr. De Vinck? You spoke about the magic sound tonight. It is what I heard in my grandmother's voice when I was a child. It is what is in the crow or in the lonely man shoveling snow, right?" Laura Denisovich turned her scarred face away from the dim light. "One afternoon my grandfather returned unexpectedly from his business trip and found my grandmother reading Pushkin to me on the stoop. He raged about the czar, grabbed an ax that leaned like an innocent sailor against the house, and then my grandfather, he began to chop the steps. He pulled the book from my grandmother. She stood in silence.

"Once the steps were in a splintered pile, my grandfather lit the broken wood and tossed the book of poems into the flames. I jumped into the fire to retrieve the book. I stumbled, and my face smacked into the flames and glowing wood. I wish to tell you this. Some people, they still read. I read Pushkin, the magic sound."

Laura Denisovich asked me to autograph my book of essays, which I did, and then she said, "Please, you touch my face?"

I was embarrassed until the old woman reached over, took my hand, and placed it against the rough part of her cheek. Then Laura Denisovich walked away and disappeared into the darkness, and I drove home. . . .

We cannot be afraid to choose what is righteous, to confront the darkness with our smooth hands gently placed upon a disfigured face of a woman who comes up to us in the night with the gold flames of burning poetry illuminating the scars of the powerless Devil.

PEOPLE CALL IT CAMPING

By Heather Harpham Kopp

Every year around June all my friends start talking about the fun they'll have camping with their kids over summer vacation. And every year around June I begin frantically checking into the campaign for year-round school.

I confess. I have a bad attitude about one of America's all-time favorite family activities.

Correct me if I'm wrong, but isn't there something inherently insane about packing up half your house only to unpack it again for a few days in mosquito-infested woods, only to pack it back up again so you can take it home only to unpack it all over again?

I used to think my aversion to camping was something carried over from childhood. My only camping memory is of the time our family got lost, arrived at a park in total darkness, and set up our leaky tent by a lake just in time for a monsoon.

But since becoming a parent, I've tried to change my attitude for the sake of my kids. Just last summer I planned a spur-of-the-moment camping trip. It would be our family's first go-it-alone adventure.

I spent all day Friday, one of the hottest of the summer, packing up our van. I was a martyr, a saint. I hunted the storage room, I ravaged the garage. My two boys followed me around in amazement, alternately exclaiming to one another, "We're going camping!"

When my husband got home, he looked impressed, thanked me for my effort, and proceeded to pack the entire van all over again—properly. We squabbled a bit, rounded up the kids, and took off. We were destined for a good time. We were doing it, the all-American family thing.

An hour down the road, the boys realized they hadn't eaten dinner yet and became convinced they'd surely starve before we reached camp. We had plenty of food. But my husband had repacked it beneath the tent and bikes and sleeping bags and surely it'd be too hard to reload it all properly. . .

So we stopped at McDonald's. A half hour later, we were back on the road. Our spirits lifted. We were going camping! We had several sites in mind. We drove to the first one, a well-known spot. It was full. "Too bad you guys weren't here about fifteen minutes ago," said the ranger. So much for fast food.

We drove on. The kids got a little antsy. When will we be there? Park number two. Full. It was getting dark now. We had one last place in mind. It was a bit of a drive, but we decided to risk it.

We were in luck! The attendant said he thought there was a spot still available. We drove through the grounds, locating the last vacant site in time to watch a smug-looking elderly couple with a fancy mobile home whip into it.

Don't misunderstand. There were other camping sites, all up and down the highway—if you didn't care about bathroom facilities, running water, a picnic table, a trail, or any recreational outlets. If you wanted a place to park your car, make yourself dirty and miserable and bored, and sleep on bumpy pine needles and rocks, there were lots of spots.

We arrived home around 1 a.m. The boys had fallen asleep in the car, flashlights in hand. We carried them in, thankful their entire world wouldn't fall apart until they awoke in their own beds tomorrow morning. Amazingly, it didn't hit them until they were on their second bowl of cereal that they were supposed to be in the woods somewhere.

Tom and I thought about being coy. "Sure we went camping! Don't you boys remember?" We'd say this with serious faces. "Yaaah. We roasted marshmallows, Noah, and you burned yours. We went swimming and fishing. Remember that huge fish you caught, Nathan? Too bad we had to let it go...."

It's not hard to guess how I spent my Saturday. Unpacking. In the heat. Putting away the lantern I'd finally located. The stakes to the tent I'd almost forgotten. The sleeping bag I worried Nathan might have wet last time he slept at a friend's.

Actually, the boys didn't take it as hard as I thought they would. Maybe it was because we pitched our tent in the yard for them to sleep in that night. Or maybe it was because of the promise we made them. A promise I'm worried they haven't forgotten. A promise I'm scared we'll have to keep this summer.

Please, somebody, save us a spot!

Our-Sized Thanksgiving

By Shannon El-Sokkary

I'm making lasagna," I quipped to a friend who had asked me what I was doing for Thanksgiving. "Unless I decide to order a pizza," I sighed, under my breath. It seemed I just couldn't get anything together now that I was a stay-at-home mother of two children. My son was just three months old, and learning to mother two children was harder than I had bargained for.

At my own mother's table we had always eaten from a set of pink floral china, the ones that she always remembered that she'd bought for a song at an estate sale. "Uncle Don, will you have apple, pumpkin or mince pie?" she'd ask.

"One of each!" he'd chortle, his standard reply. I was homesick for all that. But Mom and Dad's home was 3,000 miles away, and my husband was working the holiday. It was only a four-day weekend, but I was dreading it. Somehow, the decision to stay at home full-time and the addition of a second child had raised my expectations of the holidays to Rockwellian proportions.

I was willing to settle for an invitation to dinner with friends. But none had come, and that year I was too proud to admit how lonely I felt. I had thought of reaching out to help the less fortunate, but waiting to call until the Tuesday before Thanksgiving had narrowed my options to none that I could do with the kids.

By the time we arrived at the grocery store Wednesday morning I was exhausted altogether. Helping my children out of the van was a great effort. My daughter was as heavy, I thought, as the 25 pound turkey I wouldn't need because we were alone this year. I was starting to laugh at my own pity party as I lifted my son into the shopping cart. At least it was raining, I thought, a reminder that God knew how gloomy I felt.

I might have turned around and gone home right then if I didn't know I would be hard pressed to make dinner with the ramen noodles, diced beets and coconut milk that were left in my cupboard. We'd fallen off our weekly shopping routine since the baby was born. "Just help me make it through this day," I prayed, hoping not to run into anyone complaining that they didn't have enough room at their table for all their guests.

Inside the store, of course, the only items on sale were turkey day fixings. But we were just two adults, a finicky preschooler and a breast-fed baby. And I was in a Holiday Funk. If I couldn't have the whole thing, it seemed, a part of me didn't even want to acknowledge this holiday.

But then I got a revelation, right there in the frozen food section. Cornish hens. Yes! We were a little family with little children. Why not make a tiny turkey? I picked up my pace and gathered the ingredients we'd need. My son kicked his little legs and gave me a drooly, toothless grin. Unaware of the reason, even he knew the mood had changed.

On Thanksgiving morning we kissed Daddy "bye-bye" and settled down to watch the Thanksgiving Day Parade together. "Let's leave our jimmies on a little longer," I told the kids. "We don't have to be anywhere today." At that moment, contentedly watching marching bands pass by, I realized that I had never thought of it as a day of leisure. Thanksgiving was a production, a homemade production of four or five from-scratch pies, a huge turkey and all the trimmings. It was a party, a loud, laughing party full of family remembrances of the good old days. What I had now was my own Thanksgiving. It was a quiet, grateful moment, short on tradition, perhaps, but long on the promise of wonderful things to come. A peace came over me and my homesickness was gone.

After the parade, my daughter and I had a great time cutting circles of pre-made pastry and filling them with mincemeat (from a jar) to make tasty little tarts. I roasted the Cornish Hens next to baby carrots and little potatoes, laughing to myself. In front of me were a perfect little Thanksgiving for our family and a victory for my first holiday as a homemaker.

NEITHER FOREIGNER NOR SAVAGE

By Elisabeth Elliott

There were some very long days in the jungle when the Aucas all went off fishing or planting and left us entirely alone. There were peaceful nights when they fell asleep early and I lay in my hammock by the embers and read by candlelight. Sometimes it was the Bible. Sometimes it was the transcription of an Auca tape. Other times I read an American news magazine, dropped to me from the airplane. Suddenly a night breeze or a moth put the candle out and I was jerked from the pages of that world—the world of art, books, business, education—back to this one, this moonlit jungle clearing, the quiet people asleep with their feet over the fires, the little girl who was a part of both worlds, rolled in her blanket on a bamboo bed beside me.

"In a universe suddenly divested of illusions and lights, man feels an alien, a stranger," said Albert Camus. When the candle went out and pictures were no longer visible, when the shrill cacophony of the jungle night rose again to my consciousness and I saw those feet in the fireglow, I wanted some reconciliation, some clarification. On what plane would these worlds be reconciled? I asked God for the answers, and tried to learn what He wanted to teach me through

142

this insulation: insulation from my own world by distance, insulation from the Auca world by lack of communication.

They had been called savage. Their habitat was known in the travel ads as the "Green Hell." I was called a missionary. I must communicate.

The "Green Hell" proved to be a paradise at times, although I never appreciated the mold, mildew, or mud of the jungle. I did love the towering trees, the delicate fungi, the endless display of bromeliads and mosses, ferns and flowers, the clear-running streams, the jewel-colored sunbirds. I did not like living in a house with no walls, but I loved having no housework to do. I missed the stimulation of conversation in my own language, but I was fascinated by the mysteries of a new one. I longed to put on a dress and high heels once in a while, but I was grateful for the carefree ease of Quichua skirt and blouse and bare feet. I wished Valerie had some playmates who would not always submit to her will, but I did not overlook the invaluable experiences she was having—simplicity is the purest breeding. For everything that I would have called an inconvenience there was compensation if I took the time to look for it and had the grace to be grateful.

I watched the people I had called savages. Somehow immortal in their nakedness, speaking together in the subdued tones used among Indians, laughing childishly over small things, interested in the tiniest events about them, they seemed a lovely contrast to the elaborate dress, the loud voices (the Quichuas do not say that we "speak" English—we "shout" it), the sophisticated humor, the world-consciousness of our civilization. There were other times when their crudeness, their limited interests, their incomprehensible language, their everlasting meddling with my possessions and my affairs, their pitilessness, and their abject poverty of soul depressed me terribly.

What did it really mean to be a missionary? Never mind the definitions I had held for six previous years of missionary work. I had to start over again, from scratch. If we call ourselves followers of Jesus, obviously we must walk the path He walked. "The Son of Man came not to be ministered unto, but to minister." We must get this straight. We have come, not to be benefactors, but to be *servants*. "Slaves" is the word Jesus often used. Our perception of this truth will make an incalculable difference in our attitude toward the people, which in turn cannot help but affect their attitude toward us. To be a bene-factor is to be a superior. Quite apart from the rightness or wrong-ness, morally, of this view, I became aware that it was a bad mistake.

To the Auca I was not a superior by any standards. To be a ser-vant is to be an inferior, and unless we are willing to accept this posi-tion we are not followers of Jesus Christ. The servant is not greater than his lord. And lest we think there is some merit in what we do, we are reminded that when we have done all we are still "unprof-itable." We are in debt. We owe it to Christ, we owe it to men, sav-age or civilized, to lay down our lives daily.

I had understood this only very dimly when I went to live with the Aucas. I had worked before among Indians who had known the white man and his ways and had to some degree at least bowed to the white man's "superiority." The Auca had no such idea. He had not a reason in the world for thinking of us as his betters, and he probably had some very valid reasons of his own for thinking of us as inferiors. But from all appearances, he accepted us in the beginning as equals. This was what I had thought I had wanted. Something happened one day which illuminated to me the falsity of my own position.

I was sitting in my leaf house with a clay pot near at hand. Two old women were in the house a few yards away. "Gikari!" one of them called, in the urgent half-whisper which is their way of shout-ing. "Bring that pot here." It was my pot but I took it to her. "Well—don't bring it *empty*. Go get some water in it."

I had to go down to the river by means of a log which lay at a steep angle, fill the pot, and carry it (it had no handles and was very heavy) back up the slippery log. The old woman took it without a word.

I pondered what I had meant before when I had talked about a desire to be "accepted." I had meant that I wanted to enjoy all the benefits of being a member of their society without its obligations, as well as the benefits of being a foreigner without its opprobrium. After all, I realized now, why shouldn't Dyiku order me to bring her water? She was an older woman. In Auca society she had a right to order the younger.

This helped me to understand a little better the position of a missionary. My reason for being a missionary was one of the few things I had never doubted. I knew one thing—I must obey God, and I believed this was the thing He meant me to do, just as He meant others to be fishermen, tax collectors, draftsmen, housewives. The role seemed incidental. The goal was all-important.

There remained the message which I had to communicate. In a sense, all that we did while living with the Aucas was an attempt at communication. To eat what they ate, to live in the same kind of house, to swim and fish with them, to teach them to blow up a balloon or whistle on their fingers, to learn to spin cotton thread or weave a hammock as they did, to listen hour after hour after hour to their stories and try to write down what they said—all this was communication, the attempt to understand, to relate ourselves to them and to reach as far as possible across the chasm which separated us. Many times this seemed a naïve hope. Many times I despaired of ever really knowing them, the secrets of their hearts. Then I realized that I did not know my own heart. In this we were one.

The Aucas are men. Human beings, made in the image of God. Macdonald said, "No matter how His image may have been defaced in me, the thing defaced is His image—an image yet, that can hear His Word." We have a common source, common needs, common helps, a common end. Carl Sandburg observes that we are "alike in all countries and tribes in trying to read what sky, land, and sea say to us. . . . Alike in the need of love, food, clothing, work, speech, sleep, fun—needs so alike, so inexorably alike." The lucid recognition of the Auca as my kinsman was at the same time a new acknowledgment of Jesus Christ, of our common need of Him.

BEAT THE CLOCK

By Ellen Goodman

I have taken time off. Literally. The watch that straps my workaday wrist to its demands sits on the kitchen shelf.

I have shed its manufactured time, its minute hand, hour hand, just the way I shed my city wardrobe, makeup, panty hose, skirt. Gradually, I have even begun to lose track of time. First the minute and then the hour, finally the day. My watch and I have wound down.

I reckon my real vacation from the moment I forget whether it is Thursday or Friday. And the moment I realize that it doesn't make any difference. At last, I tell myself, I have slipped out of one time frame and sunk into another one. I have left a world divided by nothing more than numbers, sixty minutes, twenty-four hours, seven days a week. I have entered a world of seasons: blueberry, raspberry, blackberry season; lobsters that shed old shells and then harden new ones.

My daily life here is more connected to the tide than the time. At low tide I can harvest the mussels that lie under great heaps of seaweed clinging to rocks by their umbilical beards. At high tide the mackerel may swim in hot pursuit, into the cove. The cove is not a store with hours set by its owner.

Like most people in the Western world, I have grown up in the artificial environment of modern society. It's a place dominated by external timekeepers, calendars, schedules, clocks. Our lives are subdivided into fiscal years, academic years, weekdays, weekends, deadlines. We are taught that there is a time to get up, a time to go to work, a time to eat. We set the clock by a single standard.

Time orders our lives and, inevitably, orders us around. We are so removed from natural rhythms that we rarely confront how "unnatural" this is. How unnatural to strap time on.

We didn't always live with this artificial timing. In *Time Wars*, Jeremy Rifkin explains how recently people have been alienated from natural rhythms to those of the schedule, the clock, and now the computer with its nanosecond culture.

The schedule—that control on our lives—was the invention of the Benedictine monks whose early passion for organizing and filling every minute of the day grew from St. Benedict's warning that "Idleness is the enemy of the soul." His followers reintroduced the Roman hour and invented the mechanical clock.

Not until the fifteenth century did clocks, those icons of temporal time, begin to rival churches in the city squares. Not until the seventeenth century did clocks have a minute hand. "Medieval time," writes Rifkin, "was still sporadic, leisurely, unpredictable and above all tied to experiences rather than abstract numbers." It was the merchants and factory owners who eventually, and with great difficulty, trained workers—those who had previously lived in accord with the seasons—to become as regular as clockwork.

Today, writes Rifkin, "The high achievers see time as an obstacle to overcome, an enemy to defeat. They equate faster and faster learning with victory over time; to win is to beat the clock."

Is it any wonder that many of us choose vacations that stretch uninterrupted from sunrise to sunset, choose to reenter the natural cycle, days of idleness, that friend of the soul? Is it any wonder that we seek, for just a while, not to think of time as a commodity to be spent, saved, wasted, used, but to live from tide to tide?

My own escape is hardly complete. A creature of habit more than habitat, I have yet to spend a day without once looking at a clock or asking the hour. My vacation itself is circumscribed. I have only a certain amount of time allotted to timelessness. It will end at a pre-determined moment. I will go home according to the boat schedule, right on deadline.

But on this day, the ghostly white impression left by the watch on my arm has finally browned. I can barely see its imprint on my life.

—August 1987

THE BOOK OF NATURE

By Luci Shaw

L ast summer, with eleven other intrepid souls, I joined a wilderness expedition—actually a graduate-level summer-school course with the title *Creation, Wilderness, and Technology*—among the South Gulf Islands of British Columbia. During the week we rowed an open boat for 120 miles, camping every night on a different island. Though the week chosen for the trip fell in what was usually one of the driest periods of the year, it rained most days and our clothes, sleeping bags, and the contents of our duffel bags grew steadily soggier. Unloading the boat to land for meals or to set up camp for the night, we often had to form a human chain in water up to our waists before climbing the slippery, seaweed-covered rocks to high ground, and then reverse the whole process next morning as we re-embarked. The twice-daily coastal tides were fierce, surging back and forth between the islands, and as often as not we found ourselves rowing hard against the current. Besides the practical aspects of the trip—cooking meals under primitive conditions, setting up and taking down tents—we needed to find time to read assigned texts on the environment, ecology, the theology of creation, as well as to keep a detailed personal journal and engage in discussion of the issues we recognized and faced.

Though the experience was rigorous and I often felt stretched to my limits (at sixty-seven I was the matriarch of the group), I discovered that the environment of wild and rugged beauty brought me into contact with God in a surprisingly immediate, penetrating, and life-changing way. God was calling me to a level of awareness that was new to me. It was a purgative, cleansing time. There were no comfort zones between me and the creation. I was drenched by the rain and sea water, chilled by the wind, burned by the sun (when it shone—and in a small, open ship's boat there is no escape from it), exhausted by hours of rowing against the tides (and in the process developing *incredible* upper body strength!), yet thrilled, no exhilarated, by the satisfaction of challenging the elements and coming out feeling heroic. I had, and have, a new respect for creation's large-ness and raw magnificence. I wrote in my journal: "I am face-to-face with the handiwork of God and am left humbled and almost breathless with admiration."

Nature is God's great revelation of himself, his richness, his complexity, his intelligence, his beauty, his mystery, his great power and glory. God's fingerprints, the hints and clues to his nature, are everywhere.

John Stott has said: "God has written two books—the Book of Scripture and the Book of Nature." Next to my Bible, this is the realm where I experience God at work most powerfully. In fact, such an experience may be even more potent for me than the written Word because it is so freshly immediate. I take it in firsthand, with all my senses. I am not just reading a story about wandering in the wilderness. I have wandered there myself, feeling fatigue and hunger as well as exuberance and wonder.

It is also a joy to worship God in the riot of green and color around my house. I read Paul's ecstatic hymn at the end of Romans 11 as translated by Eugene Peterson, in *The Message:*

Everything comes from him;
Everything happens through him;
Everything ends up in him.
Always glory! Always praise!
Yes. Yes. Yes.

This has become my own song as well as Paul's. It is the credo of the *via affirmativa,* the life of celebration.

Sometimes it is only in memory that such worship is possible—when I'm in some bustling, crowded convention center or in a sterile hotel room on a business trip. That is where remembering (and journal keeping) comes to the aid of faith. Imagination is like a videotape on which the memory of green and the sounds of leaves and water are recorded. I play it again and again, and I can repeatedly recapture my sense of God's powerful presence by imaginative faith.

"I WANT TO WRITE!"

By Karen Burton Mains

I will not throw the bust of Shakespeare," I vowed. David had given it to me years before as an anniversary present. *I will not throw any-thing. Throwing things is an immature, senseless way of expressing anger.*

A shopping excursion had taken me from home for a few hours, and now I was paying for it. A mother always pays for release-time from housework. My pleasant luncheons planned for the very purpose of getting-away-from-it-all were always spoiled when I returned to the ruins. Although the house hadn't been immaculate when I left, it had been an hour away from the verge of being clean. Now it would take the better part of the evening to repair.

Under control, I gave Will Shakespeare's bald pate a pat and waded through tinker toys and puzzles to survey the devastation in the kitchen. *That was too much.*

Spilled sugar and flavored punch mix gummed in a pinkish mess on the floor. Sticky forks and spoons, haphazard dishes, and an entire cupboard emptied of glasses, each sitting half full assaulted my only recently calmed sensibilities. A baby food jar of pureed spinach was handily within reach on the high chair. I winged it with all my might against the upper right-hand corner of the farthest cupboard of the kitchen, marched upstairs, slammed the door, flung myself on the bed, and waited for the inclination to destroy to pass.

My children still talk about "the time Mommy threw the jar of spinach." Maybe that is because for once they had to clean up after me! I certainly demonstrated to them the scientific principle of ejection. The projectile sailed one way, but the contents of the projectile splattered a creamy green slime in the opposite direction—onto the dining room carpet, the stuccoed wall, the mirror over the buffet. I found dried spinach on the doorway months later.

Through the years I have succumbed to this inclination to throw things. Three pans with craggy stumps in place of handles hide in the cupboard and are awkward to use during meal preparation. I keep them to remind me of useless passion.

The first was tossed during year two of our marriage, when my husband invited last-minute company, people I had never met, much less had the chance to learn to love. It was not the invitation that was really the problem, though, it was the circumstances. The baby was fussing, there wasn't enough food, and the minutes were marching in double time across the kitchen clock—all demands I hadn't yet developed the stamina to cope with. I had winged the pan against the counter and watched it bang one way while the handle bounced another. In cool dismay I thought, "This is rather an expensive way to vent emotion."

So goes the tale of the saucepan. The skillet, however, went flying during a two-year-old's marathon temper tantrum which was going on its second hour. I guess I thought it was legal for Mommy to have a temper tantrum too. The third pan I can't remember throwing, although the odds were that I was probably fuming over something done by my husband.

To be fair to myself, I feel compelled to make it clear that I never threw these items *at anyone*, only in empty rooms laden with my own tension.

Reaction to my throwing arm has been mixed. My father, I suspect, thought it was kind of cute. He has always operated from the theme that the more ornery I was, the better were my chances for survival. At any rate, he gave me a cast-iron skillet one Christmas with the explanation, "Here, sweet. Here's one you won't be able to break." I have a Deep South friend with some dish-demolishing experience of her own who expresses reasonable logic, "Bettah bre-ak a dish than bre-ak a ha-id!" My mother and children think a parent should act like a parent.

David has never paid too much attention to these emotional demonstrations. His tolerance of me through the years has been exceptional. I do think it's interesting to note, however, that the jar of junior baby food was the last thing I ever pitched. Maybe this is because it was also the first time David, my husband, sat me down, dared to endure my scathing glances, and asked, "Why are you so angry?"

We sat in the living room, my husband and I, while the light from the March dusk filtered through the rooms with a softness, making the toys and havoc and my reaction seem, if not absurd, at least a little silly.

As I calmed down, I gave an explanation that seemed to me to be obvious. I was angry because the house was in a mess, and I would have to clean it again. I was always cleaning and everyone was always messing. It seemed as though I spent my entire life picking up after people. I would *never* be able to do the things I really wanted to do!

"What is it you really want to do?" he continued, probing.

On the surface that query does not seem to bear much weight. In actuality, it brought me profoundly to terms with myself. I responded quickly. The answer was on the tip of my soul. *I wanted to write.*

To write. To write. To write. To spill some of the building overflow of emotion and thoughts and feelings that dammed within me. To wind my way through those inner labyrinths and find the exits, then tell about my journey on paper. To observe joy—the pain and delight of it—then express it. To impregnate a word with meaning, then give it birth. To mold phrases, manipulate rhythms—to give them flesh. To breathe print into life—then plant it in the soul of another.

I knew what I really wanted to do.

He was quiet for a while, then asked, "What is stopping you? What can I do that will help you? Are the children and I keeping you from writing? Are you angry with us?"

Why is it some awakenings are slow buddings—like unexpected flowers unfolding? And why is it that some come tumbling like avalanches which almost destroy us with their impact?

This awful moment of truth was the tumbling kind—it was not husband or offspring or house that were stopping me. They were only the excuses beneath which I hid. *It was I—I myself—who was keeping me from writing.*

It was my sin, my very own, the sin which always popped to mind when preachers pointed fingers—procrastination. It was again the lack of discipline which had haunted me since childhood, my fatal flaw of putting things off. Though I had taken myself to task during my fourth pregnancy, and though I had established order, finally, in the household, I had not as yet benefited from all that effort! I had been frittering away the months since that child was born.

I was my own worst enemy, my own greatest deterrent. It was myself with whom I was deeply, inexorably at war. In bare, bald self-confrontation, I realized *I was angry with me!*

Moments of truth come rarely, and when they do, they are precious. One had best heed their intimate revelations. I dragged the typewriter out onto the dining room table and set up my office in the center of the house. I learned to write with toddlers crawling at my feet. I developed the capacity to hold an idea while I attended to a crisis or paused to stick dinner in the oven. I kept the writing going in my mind while I picked up toys and soothed siblings, and then rushed back to get it out on paper before the concepts were gone. I developed the capacity to concentrate in the midst of any kind of confusion. I learned to write at night when the house was quiet, and to write in the afternoon when the infants were napping, even though I have always realized that mornings were the best time for my creative effort. There were to be no excuses!

Finally, with the initial flush of early successes upon me, I set apart a small closet in the master bedroom, 4-1/2' by 3-1/2', for my writing nook, found an interested editor, began sending out free-lance material, hired a housekeeper to come in three afternoons a week, and hoped to God I would make enough money to pay her.

PART 6

Darkest Just before Dawn
Faith

I WANT TO BE LIKE JAY

By Louise Tucker Jones

I was staring at my things-to-do list. In a few weeks our son Aaron was getting married in Iowa. My husband and I had decided to make the 16-hour drive with our youngest son, Jay, who is mentally handicapped and has a severe heart condition that requires him to sleep with an oxygen tube. Now I was having second thoughts about subjecting Jay to all that travel. *What if. . .?* I kept thinking. I was about to cancel our plans.

Jay idolizes his big brother, and despite Jay's phobia about unfamiliar places, he insisted he wanted to go to the wedding. He was absolutely thrilled at the prospect of wearing a tuxedo. But he didn't fully comprehend the medical dangers that might arise.

"The cardiologist approved the trip," my husband kept reminding me—provided we didn't fly. My fears tormented me day and night. I asked God if we were doing the right thing. What if Jay had a severe panic that led to a heart attack? How would we handle a medical crisis so far from home?

"Get cardiologists' names from Jay's doctor," I scrawled at the top of my list. *I've been praying about this for days. Why can't I feel at peace?*

As our departure date drew near, I checked off the tasks I'd completed. But my litany of worries lengthened. I tossed and turned in bed. We were leaving in a week. *Lord, I don't think I can go through with it.*

The next morning, I found Jay in the hallway, rummaging through scraps of material in my sewing closet. He pulled out two pieces of fabric, explaining that they were to be made into a suit and tie for his Ken doll. I sighed. "Jay, honey, I don't know . . ." I had made simple pants and pullovers for Ken, but never a suit. Besides, there wasn't time.

Jay neatly spread the material on the floor, right in front of the closet. Then he went to the living room. I followed. "Honey, we need to talk about this."

Jay flipped on the TV and flopped on the couch. "Suit and tie," he said. "Ken."

"But I don't know if I can make a suit and tie. It's complicated."

Jay looked at me with complete confidence, then went back to watching TV. My hesitation hadn't fazed him a bit.

I walked down the hall, past the fabric on the floor, to my room. *If I don't pick it up, Jay will get the message.*

After his TV program ended, I heard Jay in his room, then back at the sewing closet. *He's given up!* I thought, relieved. After Jay had gone, I peeked out of my room. Not only was the fabric still in the same spot on the floor, but a naked Ken doll now lay beside it!

I scooped up Ken and the material and put them on the kitchen counter. It was time to change my tactics. *Maybe Jay will forget about it.*

But the next afternoon, Jay retrieved the bundle, carried it from the kitchen to my bedroom, where I keep my sewing machine, and arranged the doll and fabric on the bed. Then he sat down to wait.

I stood in the doorway, defeated by his expectant expression. "Okay, Jay," I said, popping open my sewing cabinet, "I'll try." Jay's eyes didn't betray the slightest sign of triumph. All along, he had assumed I was going to give him what he had asked for—even after I had ignored hint after hint. "You have some kind of trust in my sewing, Jay. Here goes."

Jay sat patiently on the bed while I cut and measured; he sang songs while the sewing machine hummed. An hour later we slipped the finished product on Ken. The little suit fit, and Jay was delighted—but not surprised. I was happy. With Jay satisfied, I could get back to my to-do list.

And back to my worries. *What I wouldn't give for some of my son's trusting spirit* . . . Suddenly Jay's faithful nature overwhelmed me. He had made a request, brought it directly to me, and waited expectantly. I didn't fulfill his want immediately, but he never doubted that I would.

I threw down my things-to-do list, bowed my head and closed my eyes. For a long time I just sat. Then I asked, "Father, let me be like Jay. You know my worries and my fears. Let me entrust them to you."

A few days later, after a safe and peaceful journey, we all beamed as Aaron and his beautiful bride, Amy, met at the altar. My husband and Jay (and Ken too) were handsome in their wedding suits. I was so proud of my boys.

What if my "what ifs" had kept us from this joyous moment? As the bride and groom exchanged vows, I promised myself that the next time I made a list of things to do before a big occasion, one item would be written boldly at the top: Trust. Because I want to be like Jay.

LETTING GO

By Dale Hanson Bourke

"Mommy, I did it!" Chase yelled as he burst through the front door. I leaned over the upstairs railing and saw his beaming face and tousled hair.

"I rode my bike all by myself," he announced, gasping excitedly. "Come watch."

I dropped what I was doing and ran down the stairs and out to the front porch. While his father stood on the sidewalk, Chase climbed on his bike and began peddling. He wobbled from side to side and then, just as he seemed about to fall, he took off down the street, the picture of confidence. For a split second he took his eyes off the sidewalk ahead and flashed me a big smile.

"See!" he said triumphantly.

Tom and I clapped and cheered his success.

"You did it!" we yelled, thrilled that our son had conquered this obstacle.

The victory had been hard earned. For months he had been frustrated in his attempts to conquer the two-wheeler. Time after time I would run down the street stooped over as I held on to the back of his bicycle seat.

"Don't let go!" he'd remind me nervously.

And then, after one more unsuccessful day, he'd drag his bike home dejectedly and announce, "I'm the only kid in the whole world who can't ride a two-wheeler."

I understood his feelings. I still remember the day that all my friends took off down the street on their shiny bicycles, and I was too ashamed to bring out mine because it had training wheels. And I remember the sweet victory of conquering that bicycle and sailing down the block for the first time. I wanted that sense of freedom for Chase, and yet I was sad to realize that he'd never again say, "Don't let go."

It's a tricky business, this holding on and letting go. I have yet to find its rhythm. But in my nearly seven years of parenting I have discovered that the holding on is the easy part. It's the letting go that fills me with dread and self-doubt. What if I let go too soon? But part of me fears that I won't let go at all, stifling the child who needs to grow into a man.

"Yes, you can sleep over at Peter's house," I say, proud of myself for opening this door for my son.

But then the doubts begin to roll in like waves, and I can hardly catch my breath. What if the boys begin to wrestle on the bunk beds and Chase falls off? What about the creek behind Peter's house? What if. . . ? I take a deep breath and fight my urge to hold on to my son. Instead I do what has become a daily habit. I pray for guardian angels to surround him and protect him. And then I ask for peace and wisdom. Clinging is not the answer, I know, but I need divine help to unclench my grip.

I am ashamed to admit how little I prayed before I had children. I was gliding through life, occasionally offering thanks or requesting a favor. Now prayer is all I have when I feel the need to hold on but see the importance of letting go. Prayers go with my children when I'm not there. I take comfort in imagining God's open palms beneath my children as they climb, his gentle touch easing them away from danger, his steady hand guiding them as they ride down the street. When I can't—or shouldn't—hold on I ask him to be there for me. Some days it is all that keeps my mother love from smothering the flicker of independence that deserves to be fanned.

On one hand, I am surprised that letting go is so hard for me. I have always been an independent person who ran from suffocating friendships and expected routines. I understand this need my children have to test their wings. And yet the mother in me recognizes the vulnerability inherent in independence, the headiness of freedom that can scoff at caution. I have so little control as a mother. It is the lesson God is teaching me over and over again.

As I tuck Chase into bed he says, with six-year-old bravado, "Riding my bike was easy, Mom."

I smile as I think about the number of times I went to bed with backaches, the many times the training wheels came off only to be put back on.

"Yes, it is easy once you know what to do," I agree.

Leaning over to me conspiratorially, he drops his voice.

"You want to know my secret?"

I nod, waiting.

"I just pretended that Daddy was still holding on to the back of my bike, and then I wasn't scared. That's how I learned to ride all by myself."

I hug my son and marvel at his words. And just for a moment I think I feel a gentle hand on my shoulder, steadying me as I stumble along this path of motherhood.

"Trust me," he seems to whisper. I take a deep breath and try to let go.

LAST NIGHT, TONIGHT

By Evelyn Bence

Last night I dreamt
I walked across a stream
On a bridge made of flowers.
Chains of daisies arched
Bank to bank
And I stepped out on petals
Soft as flour,
Hoping they would be
Strong as flooring.

When I reached the far side I woke,
Knowing You'd held my weight
As I walked over the border
Between yesterday and tomorrow.
You carried me last night.
I trust You with tonight.

HELPFUL HURTS

By Elisa Morgan

Eva sat on the crinkly paper of the examination table and giggled, legs stuck out straight, anchoring her in place. Teething drool dribbled down her baby chin as she chewed on the ribbon of her dress. We played peek-a-boo as we waited for the doctor to enter, examine and pronounce her "perfect" at her 12-month well-baby checkup.

"Perfect" she was. As the doctor exited, she waved instructions to a nurse for an immunization. Yikes! I'd forgotten: the shot. The nurse returned, needle and swab in hand, and twinkled her eyes at my darling baby girl. Eva twinkled back.

Until she saw the needle. Suddenly her well-anchored body became a spinning top as she made for escape. The nurse and I reacted simultaneously—she went for the torso, I lassoed the legs.

Wrestling-style, we pinned Eva to the table while I cooed soothingly from my position at her toes.

That's when it happened. My daughter, who had all her life turned to me for security, for confidence, for feedback on the environment about her, lifted her head and locked eyes with me from her paralyzed position. Her look pierced my heart, asking, "How can you let her do this to me?"

All at once an urge arose in me to tackle the nurse, grab Eva in my arms and hurdle the chairs across the waiting room in exit. What was I thinking—exposing my precious baby girl to such pain and suffering? How would she ever recover from her mother's betrayal? Most of my days were spent cautioning her from stepping off the sidewalk and into the street, pulling her hand from the hot stove, protecting her head from the coffee-table bump as she pulled up to stand. Shouldn't I "Supermom" it right here and intervene, rescuing her from pain and fear?

There, in the doctor's examination room, God's arm seemed to grip me, pinning me in place above my daughter. I lowered my gaze from Eva's eyes and considered. Words from Hebrews 12:11 hummed in my thoughts: "No discipline seems pleasant at the time, but painful. Later on, however, it produces a harvest of righteousness and peace for those who have been trained by it." Most of me realized that immunizations are not only necessary but life-preserving for babies. I wasn't damaging Eva, I was preserving her. Why did this feel so awful, confusing and scary?

My senses took in the swab massaging Eva's thigh, the needle expertly tapped and plunged into her flesh, a quick push and withdrawal, massaging again, and Eva's piercing cry. It was over. She reached for comfort and I gathered her against my chest. As the nurse reached around us and applied a Big Bird Band-Aid, truth elbowed its way into my mind and demanded my attention. Is it possible, I wondered, that a mother must allow her child to be hurt so that she can be helped? Could it be that a mom must sometimes resist the urge to rescue and instead stand firm in the experience of pain with her child? It is often only through pain that a child will mature.

I've often looked back on this lesson learned some 12 years ago. Yes, sometimes a mom must allow her child to be hurt so that she can be helped. I've seen it as Eva has forged new friendships with girls who weren't at first interested in being friends. It echoed back when our son, Ethan, purchased a CD unheard—only to discover it was filled with unrepeatable words and had to be destroyed, taking his hard-earned allowance with it. I've seen it in the first few days at a new school when no one would return my precious child's hellos.

At times, God, our loving Father, disciplines us so that we will grow to look like him. On other days—for our good, for our refinement, for our growth—he asks us to endure the inevitable pain of living in a fallen world. As moms, our job often requires getting out of the way and cooperating with his plans.

Yes, sometimes a mom must allow her child to be hurt in order for her to be helped.

WATCH O'ER MY FLOCK

By Ruth Bell Graham

Like other shepherds
help me keep
watch o'er my flock by night;
mindful of each need,
each hurt, which might
lead one to stray—
each weakness
and each ill—
while others sleep
teach me to pray.
At night the wolves and leopards,
hungry and clever, prowl
in search of strays
and wounded; when they howl,
Lord, still
my anxious heart
to calm delight—
for the Great Shepherd
watches with me
over my flock
by night.

—January 1978

GUARDIAN FOR ALL TIME

By Louise Tucker Jones

My teenage son, Jay, who is developmentally disabled, was enthralled last Christmas season when I brought home a new Nativity set. His alert blue eyes were immense with expectation. He snatched the package from me before I could shrug off my coat, and made a beeline for the hallway where we had cleared a spot on a side table.

"Here, Jay," I said, "let me help." Jay's disability makes communication difficult, but certainly not impossible. Actually, I have found that the arduous process of surmounting his impatience and deciphering what he is struggling to convey is often a journey of discovery for me. In the face of his limitations, there are moments of crystalline awe, when I understand Jay more clearly than I understand anything in the world.

I helped open the box, and Jay removed the tissue paper from the first figure. It was an angel. He cupped it gently in his hands and clasped it to his heart. I was certain that Jay was thinking about the angel he sees in his bedroom. He had told me about it many times: A bright angel stands guard at his doorway every night and sometimes speaks to him; on occasion the angel even plays with Jay's G.I. Joe toys while he sleeps.

Jay unwrapped each Nativity piece carefully and cuddled the baby Jesus just as he had the angel. We put up the big wooden stable, and Jay arranged the ceramic figures into a tightly clustered scene. After he went to his room to play, I did some rearranging, using the whole table to make the composition less claustrophobic. Later, though, I noticed the figures had been returned to their original spots, crowded around the manger. I spread them out again, smiling at the thought of my son playing with and marveling at the Nativity set.

The next day the figures were again huddled together, but with an odd addition. G.I. Joe had joined the group. Puzzled, I studied the scene. All the pieces—the kings, the angel, the donkey and cow, even Joe—all were as close to the Christ child as possible, shoulder to shoulder in a snug semi-circle. What was Jay up to?

That night I attached a small clip-on reading lamp to the top of the stable behind the star, pointing down. The light filtered through slats in the roof and shone directly on the infant's placid face. I turned out the hall light and called Jay.

He came running, but as soon as he saw the illuminated Nativity scene it seemed as if someone had slipped a switch and put him in slow motion. His face was alive with wonder. We knelt close together on the carpet, looking directly into the stable, and talked about that starry night. Jay reached out and patted the cow and donkey when I told him how they had warmed the baby with their breath. "Oooo..." he crooned. He touched Jesus. Then he reached for one of the adoring angels and pulled it in even closer, so that it was within the halo of light. I had left the figures the way Jay had arranged them. Now I saw the light was just bright enough to encompass them all, including the angel.

Of course! It made no sense to Jay for anyone to keep his distance from Jesus. As for G.I. Joe, to Jay the birth of our Savior was as real in time today as it was 2,000 years ago, so why wouldn't Joe be included?

Later, when I went to his room to kiss him good night, Jay was still talking about the baby Jesus. He signed "baby" and said "Jesus," then pointed at his door, saying and signing "angel." Impatiently, he re-signed the sequence, pointing emphatically at the door.

"Is your angel at the door?"

"Yes," he answered, adding: "Baby Jesus."

His eyes pleaded with me to understand.

"The angel and baby Jesus?"

Jay's whole face lit up when I caught on. He stepped to the door and looked down the hall at the Nativity scene, then back at me. "My angel and the baby Jesus," he repeated. *What is he trying to tell me?*

Suddenly I remembered the angel figure Jay had so carefully pulled into the light. With a shiver of recognition I knew, knew as clearly as I had ever known anything, what Jay was saying and what his angel had told him. I was astounded.

"Jay, your angel was really there, wasn't he? He was at the manger that night with Jesus." Jay nodded triumphantly and patted my arm in approval: "Good, Ma-ma!" It was so simple a concept I almost laughed. Angels, of course, are immortal.

I kissed him good night. As he burrowed under the covers, I said, "Honey, what you told me is very special."

That night I lay awake a long time wishing I could see Jay's angel, that I too could gaze into the face of one who had actually looked upon the newborn Son. But God reserves that sacred privilege for very special people, people like my son—who communicates from his heart because he does not have the luxury of speech.

Jay is plagued by many serious health problems, and I often tell God my worries about him. But now, when I put up the Nativity set, I am reminded again that an angel who watched over my Lord now watches over my son.

PART 7

Morning Stars

Gratitude

MAMA'S PRIDE

By Jo Kadlecek

It wasn't a crowded plane. Seats were uncommonly empty, like the stares of these early morning passengers. This would be a quiet flight, a sleepy one, where career agendas and hard good-byes would fade into three hours of unconscious travel.

Then the teenage mother with stringy hair, thick glasses, and rose-red lips walked on board. She smiled softly as she slipped through first class and into her seat back in 21D. Baby son—barely a year—was already working his mama over on this cold, quiet November morning. One seat wasn't enough for his baby blue eyes and so he wandered through 22 and 23 and back again to 21D, his tiny hands and knees in perpetual motion.

It was fun at first for Baby, and Mama kept smiling as flight attendants and businessmen cooed and cuddled him. But after take-off and orange juice and banana bread, Baby's vocal chords unfastened like the seat belts of confident passengers. Young Mama was patient, following, playing, singing, praying for anything to calm her bellowing son. The plastic pink pacifier was not enough for this wiggly, tired boy. No warm milk, no clapping games, no emergency exit cards in the seat pocket in front of them could hold his attention, or his hollers.

Stares darted past the coffee cart. Headsets went on. Little pillows and blue blankets fell over ears. Still, Mama smiled and held on for life. She was a fighter. "He is a good boy," her face apologized to anyone who glared at the noise. "My son doesn't usually cry like this. . . ."

Her silent speech, and her attempts to harness one-year-old energy, were interrupted by old, worn hands from across the aisle. The elderly woman's blue eyes matched Baby's. "He's a good boy," said the frail seventy-something woman in 22C. Her wrinkled face made more wrinkles as she threw a laugh and a kiss to Mama's pride. Fragile but firm arms underneath a brown embroidered sweater (the kind that anyone else would have given to the Salvation Army) reached across to 21D, picked up the boy, and drew him close to her.

And then a tiny miracle occurred on Flight 134.

Silence suddenly resounded throughout the cabin as thick as the baby wails that had pierced it only seconds before. Fingers barely bigger than a knitting needle began tracing the brown flowers on the elderly woman's chest. She cooed at him and whispered to him and held him tight. She rocked him and walked him and talked him all the way to first class and back.

"Take a break, honey," said one generation to another, one tired mother to another. Familiarity, like an old favorite sweater, comforted the younger caregiver, and the soft teenage smile flashed compliance to the wisdom standing before her. And for the first time in a long time, the aged woman felt . . . useful.

And so affection soothed both the one-year-old bundle and the wrinkled life holding him. So much so that baby boy finally, happily, slept. Mama rested. Elderly bones felt human again.

And absolute strangers became family for a simple, satisfying moment.

AROUND MY MOTHER'S TABLE

By Sharon Growney Seals

This year my folks are driving from Kansas to Arkansas to spend Thanksgiving with us, and I am delighted. It is a treat for me to have them here, and my dad usually loves my cooking. It's a treat for Mom too because she doesn't cook.

A lot of people think I'm kidding when I say that my mom doesn't cook. I know some people claim they can't cook simply because they derive no joy from the act, but Mother is a serious contender in the she-can't-boil-water competition. And she doesn't delude herself about her abilities either. She's the first to tell the story of how, when my dad was in medical school, she invited his friends over for a popcorn study session and didn't know to put a lid on the pan. She'll tell anyone straight out that she loathes cooking and is beyond the point of sensitivity to her kids' teasing that she is one of the few people on the planet who can convert hamburgers to hockey pucks. She's like an alchemist that way.

This ability of hers to transform food into other matter made for some interesting dinners at our house. Dad actually had to ban meat loaf from the table (I personally haven't touched the stuff since 1969). And I recollect one time when she made flavored Knox

Blocks for dessert and she misunderstood the directions. Instead of adding one packet of gelatin to the brew, she added the entire box—four packets. It is the only gelatin I've ever eaten that crunched. But I will say this: it bounced great when it hit the table. It kept us entertained for hours.

Mom had this great saying she would trot out every time one of us begged to take a bag lunch to school. "You better eat there, honey. It might be the only hot food you get today." Indeed, we lived on breakfast cereal, ate the stuff twice a day for ten years or more.

Now that I am an adult with two picky eaters of my own, I know how frustrating it must have been to feed the locusts that we were, especially since Mom didn't like to cook in the first place. Yet, her kitchen was always full of people eating. Kids—her own and others—were in her kitchen churning out a constant stream of ham and cheese sandwiches, whipping up omelets, munching apples, or reheating the brisket that Mom actually mastered somehow. In fact, I recently attended my fifteen year high school reunion and one memory I heard over and over from classmates was how great it was to eat at my parents' house.

Had my memory failed me regarding Mom's cooking inabilities? I think not. It wasn't what we ate in her kitchen that mattered; it was that we were always welcome there. My mom never used the "I'm done cooking so you're done eating" line that I tell my own children. Instead, she never batted an eyelash when my friend Kelli Kinzer made banana-butter-sugar sandwiches at her table. She didn't get all pious and preachy when we kids would make chocolate chip cookies from scratch and eat every morsel of the dough without cooking it. She'd turn a blind eye when, during football training season, my brother Dan and his friend Matt started drinking eggs in their orange juice.

Mom's greatest abilities in the kitchen had nothing to do with her ovens. Instead, she was a master at putting people at ease. A person could be a green-eyed, purple polka-dotted, bona fide picky eater, and she would graciously say, "Help yourself to whatever you can find in the fridge." And she would mean it.

Indeed, my mother's welcoming hospitality is her trademark, and it isn't limited to her kitchen. Her house is always full of two things—

good groceries and unlimited acceptance. She is a natural, gracious "gatherer." People gravitate to her kitchen for the simple reason that it is hers.

Now that I am an adult, I realize that a pilgrim could do a lot worse than to land at Trudy Growney's table. But this Thanksgiving, I look forward to relieving her of a cooking job that she doesn't relish and to having Mom and Dad sit at my table for a change. I'm not going to worry too much if my turkey is dry or my gravy is lumpy. Not all of a meal's flavor comes from its seasoning.

LIBRARY DAYS

By Susan Branch

The public library became a haven to me on hot summer days when I was about eight or nine. I spent a good part of every summer luxuriating in the air-conditioned quiet there. The library was only a couple of blocks from my house so I walked there, barefoot, and I remember how wonderful that cold, smooth floor felt on my hot little feet. I remember the way the library smelled—that good book smell and I remember walking home with my arms overflowing with romance, adventure, fantasy and inspiration. I adored fairy tales, *The Red Book of Fairy Tales, The Yellow Book of Fairy Tales, every* book of fairy tales. I loved books about big families like mine, The *All of a Kind Family* series was my favorite. When I was 15 I read *Gone With the Wind* and sobbed into my pillow at the end. I still have a copy of that sweet story *Seventeenth Summer* just for the feeling of that time of my life. Summer and books go hand-in-hand in my mind. I read on the porch swing, I read in a tree (I learned about reading in a tree from a book, of course). I read in my "secret place" (another book), I read at the beach, in the bathtub, in my bed, with my bologna sandwich, at the park and in the car. These days my favorite thing is to take my book and go out to lunch. I love finding things in old books, so now I decorate the books I like best with a flower to dry between the pages; a leftover piece of artwork to use as a bookmark; or cartoons I think are funny—so someday in the future someone will find my little things and wonder about the person who put them there. Me!

MARGARET'S STORY

By John Trent with Erin M. Healy

Awoman who is a true servant reaches out to others with movements so completely integrated into her way of life that it is often difficult to isolate a single gesture and say, "Herein lies a story." As best-selling author Ingrid Trobisch once said, "Women like to make sacrifices in one big piece, to give God something grand, but we can't. Our lives are a mosaic of little things, like putting a rose in a vase on the table."

My mother was the kind of woman who placed roses in other people's lives. In fact, she distributed her flowers so freely that many who knew her soon found themselves lying in a veritable bed of scented velvet petals. It was her way.

Distracted by the demands of a career, a ministry, a husband, and three teenagers, I did not fully realize the extent of my widowed mother's rose giving until she came to live with us. With cancer rapidly spreading throughout her body, her bright life was clearly waning. I wanted to have her close by, to celebrate her remaining days, to care for her more completely.

I suspect, however, that she did more for us than we did for her. On her good days I would catch her pressing my husband's shirts, applauding my daughter's fledgling attempts to learn the violin, or telling my son stories of Dad's football years. She filled a long-forgotten bird feeder outside the kitchen window and lured them back to visit. She cut flowers for the dining room table—how long had it been since I'd last done that?—and helped my youngest with his English assignments. While Mother was with us, our home was brighter than it had been in months.

Then she was gone, and it seemed for a moment that the brightness had gone too. But a woman like Mother can't take that kind of light with her, as became evident after the funeral.

Mrs. Knighten brought over a relish tray for the gathering after Mother's memorial. "She was a most thoughtful woman," Mrs. Knighten told me. "After my Jack passed on, she came over every day to visit and take care of my cats. Cats! Who but your mother would have thought of that? I had completely forgotten them."

Young Katie Arnold held my hand with tears in her eyes. Mother had taken Katie to church for years after her parents had divorced. "There were things I could tell your mom that I could never explain to anyone else. She understood me better than anyone ever has."

"I'll miss her," Pastor Davidson told me quietly. He gave me a handmade card signed by the kids she'd taught at Vacation Bible School. "It will be hard to find someone who can run our clothing drive as well as she could."

"She made the best chicken-noodle soup I have ever tasted! Could drive a cold away in a matter of minutes . . ."

". . . still have the rag dolls she made for our girls the year we couldn't afford Christmas presents . . ."

". . . that time she paid our utility bills until Ted could get a job again . . ."

". . . picked up Jamie from school a dozen times when I'd get stuck in meetings . . ."

". . . and she just held me and held me when I couldn't stop crying . . ."

The conversation whirled around me, and I smiled, knowing that even in her death she would inspire each of us who loved her to serve one another with the love of Christ, even as she had served us. We talked and remembered late into the night.

The next day I visited our florist and cleaned them out of their roses. "I'll take everything you have in stock," I told the startled girl at the register. "Yes, as many as you can spare." I drove to the cemetery and carried them all to my mother's grave, where the overturned earth and dozens of flower arrangements were still fresh.

"Thank you, Mother," I said aloud, laying one pink rose on top of the marker. After a few moments I took a walk around the perfectly manicured grounds, leaving a single rose on every grave that didn't boast a flower.

Roses in the name of a rose giver. Roses for those who had none. It's what she would have done.

LESSONS IN A GOLDFISH BOWL

By Joy MacKenzie

In my growing-up years, I never thought of my mother as my friend. In the 1940's and '50's, mothers were just mothers—they weren't supposed to be friends. But my mom was a maverick, and her relationship with her four children was anything but traditional. A busy preacher's wife and matriarch of the Baptist parsonage, her contributions to my father's ministry would, today, fit a composite description of Christian education director, coordinator of women's ministries, youth director, administrative assistant, and church secretary. Music was the only part of the life of the church in which she had no input—Mother was a monotone bass (no kidding) who could play only one song on the piano, and a fitting song it was: "Work for the Night Is Coming." The title spoke volumes about her life ethic.

In her "spare time" away from the family and the church, she still did some substitute teaching and continued her graduate courses. She was an insatiable learner, finally completing her master's degree at the age of fifty-five—the same summer I got mine. She had racked up sixty-some credit hours over the years. My degree represented the normal thirty-four!

If she was guilty of idolatry, words were her god. No one else's mom served poetry with breakfast. Half of our kitchen wall was a large, heavy slate blackboard on which she wrote choice snatches of Scripture and poetry that we four children were to memorize— before supper. Repetition being the law of learning in those days, she would chant and clap and overdramatize the lines with us until we were overcome, either by laughter or irascible impatience. Her solution to my boyfriend problems was, typically, to write the boys riddles or silly poems. Sometimes they contained a personal admonishment:

> Young love is an adventure
> Which is riddled with temptation,
> So this request I offer
> For your serious contemplation:
>
> Be circumspect, and try to keep
> Your hands just where you oughter
> Leave "discovery" to Columbus;
> Feast your eyes upon my daughter!

Our irritation with a gnarly parishioner was often assuaged by making the offender the subject of a saucy cooperative effort at rhyme, which we chanted with relish and uncontrolled laughter.

> Here lies Deacon Smith, so cold
> His scowl fixed, dark and dour
> The sight of children changed his air
> From satisfied to sour.
> Now relaxed and free of care,
> He spends each happy day
> Where preachers' children line the curbs
> Of Heaven's golden way!

It was this unconventional, crazy lady who shaped my image of mother, ministry, and yes, friendship. Oh, I was unaware of the influence at the time. Only decades later, when I set out to define the qualities of friendship, did I realize the benefits of what I had learned in the parsonage!

Most preachers' kids hated their "fishbowl" existence. Gloria [Gaither] and I are possibly the only exceptions I know of, and I've no doubt that our mothers made all the difference. They made the challenge of parsonage life an adventure. Our small churches were like microcosms of Dickens' novels; the whole odd spectrum of humanity dwelt therein. We were allowed to react honestly and openly to the frustrations of being preachers' kids. Through the tears and laughter, we also learned to become positively involved in the lives of other people. The hurting, the hapless, the homeless seemed to gravitate to our front door. I rarely slept in my own room; more often than not, it was occupied by a vagrant or a missionary on furlough.

One day, as my high school boyfriend and I arrived home from school, Mother met us on the porch.

"Kids!" she blurted in desperation, "I have an Indian in the bathtub!" We dissolved into laughter at the familiar tone of dramatic urgency. As the story unfolded, we learned that the man, a Mohawk Indian, had been walking five days in stormy weather, across the Straits of Mackinaw from Michigan's upper peninsula. A missionary had given him my father's name as a contact, should he need food or housing. He was cold and hungry, and his clothes were wet and soiled. What he seemed to need most was a bath, so Mom had attempted to wash his clothes while the man bathed, but they had disintegrated in the washing machine. Mom wanted us to go to the house of the missions chairman to find some suitable clothing. "Your father's clothes are too small," she said. "And hurry! The poor soul is probably shaking with the shivers!"

Daily life in the parsonage was a combination of chaotic exhilaration and serious challenge. Somehow, Mother made us feel that at the end of the bedlam, there was always a party to be enjoyed. We learned to value people and their peculiarities.

The lessons of friendship were deeply ingrained—discipline; patience; self-sacrifice; how to create fun out of frustration, persist with others through all kinds of trials, and ride over the storm, knowing that behind the clouds, the sun was always shining; accepting what is; enjoying the good times; persevering through the bad.

To my future benefit and delight, these were the early lessons of life that laid the foundation for a joyful succession of enduring relationships.

Ah, There's Good News Tonight

By Maida Heatter

The year was 1943. The country was at war. Dwight Eisenhower, Supreme Commander of the Allied Forces in Europe, was preparing for the invasion of Normandy. German submarines were sinking ships along the eastern coast of the United States; burning vessels could be seen from the Atlantic shoreline. In the South Pacific, battles were fierce; the brutal struggle for Guadalcanal was one of the worst.

The whole country had one determination—to win the war as soon as possible. Fifteen million brave men and women were in the armed services, and in one way or another, every single American was deeply involved in the war effort. Ordinary men and women were performing extraordinary feats. Automobile factories built tanks and other armaments, shipbuilders launched a ship a day, aircraft factories turned out one hundred thousand war planes in a year. Too many homes had a gold star or two hanging in the window, each star an indication that a member of the family had died in the service. Telegrams brought the terrible news: "Wounded, missing, or killed in action." Many women worked in war production factories. Housewives rolled bandages for the Red Cross and baked cookies for the local USO, the United Service Organization, which had clubs all around the country for the servicemen who were away from home.

My husband was in the army and my brother was in the navy. My year-old daughter and I lived with my parents on Long Island. My father, Gabriel Heatter, was one of the country's best-known radio news commentators. He did his broadcasts from home, where we had set up a broadcasting studio in an upstairs bedroom as well as a stand-by studio in the basement air-raid shelter. To make an ordinary room into a studio it was necessary to hang heavy drapes (even a few blankets) and to use thick rugs and upholstered furniture so that the voice did not echo or bounce off the walls. Associated Press and United Press news tickers installed in our home brought my father worldwide news twenty-four hours a day. Although an engineer came every night to handle the technical aspects of the broadcast, he taught both my mother and me what to do in an emergency if he didn't get there. Happily, we were never called upon. The broadcasts were carried across the country by about four hundred radio stations and to the armed forces overseas. A personal representative of Winston Churchill and another who was President Roosevelt's man came to lunch several times a week, every week, and they stayed, often, through dinner and through the broadcast at 9:00 p.m.

Those were nervous times—exciting, tense, scary, wonderful and terrible.

Professionally, I was a fashion illustrator. But my hobby was cooking. Especially baking cookies. I had always baked cookies, but now that there was a war on, there were a whole army and navy to bake for. I sent packages to everyone I knew in the service, and although I would have continued to bake and mail out cookies without any thank yous, when the grateful letters came in from overseas, I was totally inspired; the oven hardly ever had a chance to cool off.

When, that fall, I heard that the New York City USO wanted cookies for a big Christmas party, it was music to my ears. I baked those cookies from early until late every day for weeks. My only problem was getting enough boxes to pack them in. Food shortages and rationing (butter and sugar were strictly rationed) didn't bother me, as there were always friends and neighbors who wanted to help.

They gave me their ration coupons, they shopped for me, and they helped pack the cookies. The filled boxes lined the entrance hall and the dining room and flowed over into the living room.

The day before Christmas a neighbor piled the boxes into his truck and my mother and I went along to deliver the cookies to the USO at Times Square. Gasoline was rationed but *this* was a priority delivery.

My father always searched the news for any little item that might give hope to a worried wife or mother, and to everyone listening to his broadcast. One night when the news was especially grim—the Allied forces were losing several large battles—he found a few words on the ticker implying that the Allies might have sunk a small German ship (maybe not much more than a shrimp boat). Exaggerating a bit, he opened his broadcast with "Ah, there's good news tonight." The country needed that. Everyone listening slept better that night. Those words became his slogan. Even today, when I meet someone new, they might smile and say, "Ah, there's good news tonight." If they're old enough to remember.

On that Christmas Day—the day after we delivered the cookies— the phone rang. I answered it. And I heard the whole USO club-roomful of people all yell in unison, "Ah, there's good news tonight." I loved it, and so did my mother and father. And over the next few months I received mail from many of the men who had been there telling me how much homemade cookies meant to them. They said it was the next best thing to a trip home. I think I received more happiness out of it all than they did. That often happens with cookies; the giver gets as much as, or more than, the receiver.

If I counted the number of cookies, or the number of recipes, that special Christmas, I don't remember it now. One thing I do remember is that none of those cookies was dainty. I was baking for the army and the navy and the marines. They were all he-man cookies. The ones that had raisins or nuts had lots of them. The chocolate cookies were very chocolate. The spice cookies were very spicy. In a way, I think that one baking experience influenced everything I have baked since.

There have been many times since then when I have baked cook-ies in tremendous quantities. I baked cookies for hundreds of girls at a Girl Scout Christmas party. I baked cookies for President Reagan and six other heads of state and their staffs of hundreds at the economic summit in Colonial Williamsburg in 1983. I baked a cookie buffet for one of Craig Claiborne's sumptuous New Year's Eve parties and another for one of his monumental birthday parties. All memorable events, since to me happiness is baking cookies. But that one particular time, during the war, baking for the servicemen, was like a first love affair. Special.

...[T]he following cookies are, in fact, among those that I made that special Christmas (with minor changes and updating). They ... pack well, they store well (when wrapped airtight), and they travel well. They may be frozen (thaw before unwrapping). Correct oven temperature is essential for cookies....

Merry Christmas.

Raisin Oatmeal Cookies

Huge, soft, and chewy—with peanut butter, raisins, oatmeal, and no flour.

1-1/2 cups (8 ounces) raisins
4 ounces (1 stick) unsalted butter, at room temperature
1-1/4 cups (12 ounces) smooth peanut butter (I use Peter Pan)
1 teaspoon vanilla extract
1 teaspoon light or dark corn syrup
1 cup granulated sugar
1/2 cup dark brown sugar, packed
3 eggs graded "large"
2 teaspoons baking soda
1/2 teaspoon mace
4 cups old-fashioned rolled oats (not "instant")

Makes 22 to 24 large cookies

Adjust two racks to divide the oven into thirds and preheat the oven to 350 degrees. Line cookie sheets with parchment paper or with aluminum foil, shiny side up. Set aside.

Place the raisins in a vegetable steamer over hot water on high heat, cover, and steam for about 10 minutes. Uncover and set aside.

In the large bowl of an electric mixer beat the butter until soft. Add the peanut butter and beat until mixed. Beat in the vanilla, corn syrup, and both sugars. Then add the eggs one at a time, beating until mixed. Through a fine strainer add the baking soda and mace. Then on low speed add the oats. Remove the bowl from the mixer and stir in the raisins.

Place a length of aluminum foil on the counter next to the sink. Use a 1/4-cup measuring cup (the kind intended for dry ingredients) to measure the dough, and place the mounds any which way on the foil. Wet your hands, just shake off the water, pick up a mound of dough, shape it into a ball, and then press it to about 1/2-inch thickness and 3 inches in diameter. Place the round of dough on the lined cookie sheet. Keep your hands wet, continue to shape the cookies, and place them on the sheets at least 2 inches apart (these spread— place only 4 on a sheet).

Bake two sheets at a time, reversing the sheets top to bottom and front to back once during baking. Bake for about 18 minutes or until the cookies are golden but not until they feel firm when gently pressed with a fingertip. Do not overbake. These will firm up as they cool, and they are best if they are soft.

Let the baked cookies stand on the sheets for about a minute to firm up a bit. Then with a wide metal spatula transfer the cookies to racks to cool.

If these are not to be served soon they should be wrapped individually in plastic wrap, wax paper, or foil. Or box them with wax paper between the layers. Just don't let them dry out.

Variation: Chocolate Chunk Raisin Oatmeal Cookies

You should use about 12 ounces of semisweet chocolate—preferably the kind that comes in thin bars like Tobler Tradition or Lindt Excellence. Cut the chocolate into pieces about 1/2 inch in diameter. I use an ice pick rather than a knife to break up the chocolate. The pieces will be uneven. Follow above recipe, and add the chocolate after adding the raisins. Shape as above. (If the cookies tend to crack on the edges press the cracks together and, if necessary, move some of the pieces of chocolate from the edges to the top.) Bake as above. Serve while the chocolate is still soft or let the cookies stand until the chocolate hardens before wrapping.

Like Mother, Like Daughter

By Robin Jones Gunn

R achel came home from school today with Kristin's phone number—memorized! This is a first. I watch her march to the portable phone and say the number aloud as she dials. "Hello. This is Rachel Gunn. May I please speak to Kristin?"

She balances the phone on her shoulder, just the way I do, and begins to walk around the house. I don't look like that, do I?

"Hi, Kristin. It's Rachel." She opens the cupboard and checks for snacks, still balancing the phone.

"Nothing. What are you doing?"

She heads for the front porch with a handful of pretzels.

I call out after her, "Would you like something to drink?"

She half turns and, with a sweet facial expression and a finger touched to her lips, silently motions for me not to interrupt her. Is that what I do?

I casually follow her to the porch and nestle on the wicker love seat. I begin flipping through a magazine. Rachel's eyes meet mine, and she gives me a "don't you have anything better to do than follow me around all day?" look.

She speaks. Not to me, but to that invisible person on the phone. "I remembered your number."

She checks the hanging petunias with her free hand to see if they need water. There she is, balancing the phone on her shoulder, clutching pretzels with her right hand, and fingering the soil with her left. Just like her mother.

"Well, that's all. I guess I'll see you tomorrow at school."

She wipes her muddy finger on a leaf, still balancing the phone. Then clutching her wad of pretzels, she pulls a wicker chair toward her with her foot—just like I do.

"Okay. Bye."

I watch as Rachel pulls the phone away from her ear with her free hand, then catches a pretzel between her teeth and presses the "off" button with her nose. Just like . . .

"Do you know what?" I tell her as she joins me on the love seat and tries to fit her pre-adolescent body onto my lap. "Do you know that I think you're absolutely amazing?"

She smiles, kisses me on the tip of my nose, and says, "I know. That's 'cause I'm just like you."

WINTER'S WOOD

By Elizabeth Traff

A new snow fell,
Fresh and pristine,
Painting our world
So white, so clean.
I longed to see
Beyond my fence,
So out I trudged
Through drifts immense.
"Come!" the woods called,
And I obeyed.
I tramped through snow
Where nature played.
As birds appeared,
Their movements, swift,
Left imprints on
The downy drift.
My eyes perceived
Their acts as crude,
But without fail,
They found their food.
Those precious birds
Found shelter, too.
Snow can't disguise
What God can do.
I stood in awe
Of His design:

The tracks of birds
'Mid trees of pine.
A thousand prints
Proclaimed His care
As much for me
As birds of air.
I glimpsed His hand
And understood
God's providence
In winter's wood.

THAT'S MY BOY!

By Deena Lee Wilson

This summer Chandler was just the right age to be a ring-bearer for the first time. . . .

"I'm going to be a ringbear?" He frowned dubiously, unsure whether this strange assignment was privilege or punishment. It took a little bit of explaining. . . .

The wedding was for Scott, my husband's handsome nephew. Scott had lit the candles at our wedding nine years ago. Now Michelle had lit his life. The wedding was classic and elegant. It was white pillars and arches, trailing ivy and a limo. Before it began, I chatted with family while Chandler lounged around with Scott and the "big boy" groomsmen. I smiled as I watched him closely watching them. He was clutching a scuba-diver action figure in one hand, a yellow plastic toy from a fast food place in the other. He was Scott's twin; their black tuxes had been chosen to match.

When the ceremony began, the family was shoulder-to-shoulder in the pew. Ethan played musical laps on Alex and me. He looked darling in striped blue and white linen shorts, blue suspenders, a red polo shirt. The shorts would be too tight by the time he ate one mint at the reception, but there was no larger size, so I

had bought them anyway. After all, how many times would Scott
be getting married?

I tried to twist in the pew so I would have a clear view of everyone coming down the aisle. I felt the Velcro closure on the diaper
bag grab something. When I yanked, I discovered that Ethan's cute
white knee-highs were rapidly unraveling. I made a silent promise
that from that day on I was going to be the only one in the family
wearing hose.

Chandler marched down the aisle like a pro . . . carrying the ring
on a pillow. He was balancing it like it was Cinderella's glass slipper.
At the front, he turned, then stood rooted in place in front of the
groomsmen, the top of his head just about at their waists.

"Bend your knees," I mouthed silently. I didn't want to be a hover-
mom, but maybe I needed to be prepared to vault out of the pew
just in case Chandler toppled like a sapling in a high wind. He didn't.

The ceremony was under way and my eyes grew misty. I dabbed
at them, and it was just about then that I decided it wasn't such a good
idea having Scott and Chandler dressed in matching tuxedos. Because
I blinked and suddenly it was Chandler, not Scott, who was the groom.
He had found someone to give that glass slipper to. I blinked again
and it was not Michelle looking luminous in her gown and veil, it was
that little girl we had met at the park when Chandler was three.

I will never forget it. It was one of those rare days when everything felt so right in my world. I had renewed my driver's license and
actually liked the photo. I had stepped on the scales and discovered
I was two pounds lighter. Ethan was round and adorable at seven
months and here we were at the park, my boys and I, on a warm,
cloudless day. Chandler looked like the little prince of summer, tan
and in perpetual motion, in a red T-shirt and jeans shorts. There was
nothing I had to do; nowhere I had to be; nothing more I wanted.
The sun was on my face and I was in heaven.

Chandler broke into my reverie. "Mommy!" He was yanking on
my pants leg and he had someone in tow. "Look! I got a girl!" She
could have been his sister, standing there willowy and winsome, with
blue eyes and long blonde locks. Suddenly the two of them looked
dangerously like a matched set.

My heart skipped a beat. My mouth went dry. My mind whirled ahead to a future day, so far away, so soon. "Mommy, I got a girl!"

Yipes! Was that a tear I was blinking back? I caught myself and bent down to give a friendly mommy smile and say "Hi" to this little playmate. But she—no, they—were already gone. Isn't that just the way it happens? As I straightened, I spotted them happily running off together, hand in hand.

I blinked again and Scott and Michelle, hand in hand, were back in their rightful places as bride and groom. And Chandler had not budged from his. He was doing so well today . . . almost too well. It seemed to me he was being a little too grown-up, a tad too perfect. But then, just when I was starting to get a bit wistful and worried, something wonderful began to happen right before my eyes.

Chandler started to fidget. He began twisting his feet, standing on the sides of those uncomfortable plastic shoes. My eyes brightened. He rolled his shoulders, started looking around. My heart lifted. Then he tipped his head slowly back and gave an eyeball-rolling, tonsil-revealing yawn. I broke into a smile. Scott and Michelle's big kiss was coming and so was the end of Ringbear's endurance. Another minute and the music soared and everyone began marching joyfully up the aisle.

Chandy came tumbling up the aisle with an eager look that shouted, "Where's the cake?!" His shirttail hung out on one side like a crumpled banner. His limp boutonniere clung to his lapel like a gasping survivor. He looked messy and rumpled and ready to play. He looked *wonderful*.

I wanted to stand up and cheer, "That's my boy!" My boy. For now. He is five, not 15 or 25. I still have some years—unforgettable years—before he's the one in the big tux, giving the glass slipper and his heart away.

HALF-PINT

By Patsy Clairmont

My dad was a milkman when I was growing up, which might explain his nickname for me, "Half-Pint." His route was in the area where I attended school. I would sometimes see his truck from the window of my classroom as he delivered to his customers. One delivery stands out in my mind. . . .

The girls' gym class was playing baseball on one end of the school field, and the boys were playing at the farthest opposite point. I guess that was supposed to help us stay focused on the game and not the guys. Actually, the boys were so far from us we didn't know they were there until . . . The Big Spill.

I was playing shortstop. I think I was given that spot because I was five feet tall (maybe that was why Dad called me Half-Pint).

I certainly wasn't put in the infield because I was good at catching the ball. Any hopes of that skill developing came to an abrupt halt when I stopped a line drive with my throat. That game forever drove home the term "hard ball." Ever since, when a baseball would head in my direction, I'd sidestep it or duck.

This particular day, my team was heading for our field positions after I had made the third out. I turned to face home plate when I spotted my dad's milk truck coming down a side road toward the field.

"Dad, Dad, hi Dad!" I shouted enthusiastically and repeatedly, while jumping up and down, waving my baseball mitt.

My dad spotted me and leaned out his truck's open door to return my greeting. His truck was the kind you drive standing up. As he waved, he veered too close to the edge of an incline, and the truck slid and tipped sideways. As the truck fell to the right, my dad jumped out the door to the left just as the load of milk shifted to the front. In those days most of the milk was in glass bottles, which we could hear shattering as the cases collided.

I couldn't move. I realized my dad was safe and unhurt, but there was still the ditched truck and damaged cargo. Tears began to run down my face. I felt responsible because I had distracted him.

As I stood staring at my dad while he surveyed his "milk shake," something else began to shake. It was the earth beneath my feet. I turned to see the boys' gym class stampeding across the field toward the girls' now halted game. They ran through and around us, out to the road, and over to my dad's dairy disaster. With the strength of young men motivated by the squeals of the girls, they were able to upright the milk "cart."

My dad was so relieved he didn't have to call a tow and that the inside damage sounded worse than it was, that he rewarded the boys by throwing boxes of ice cream bars into their midst.

The boys, equally thrilled with themselves, began to run down the road (now affectionately called the Milky Way) with their reward, laughing, with the rest of the group in hot pursuit. The poor coach was winded from blowing his whistle in attempts to regroup his "milk men."

I still had not moved. I was peeking through the webbing of my mitt. My gym suit was wet with tears.

THE AMERICAN CLOTHESLINE

By Erma Bombeck

Never do I feel the sun on my face and the wind gently billowing my skirt that I do not hold my right hand over my heart and mourn the passing of the housewife's answer to Radio Free Europe: the American clothesline.

Like the American buffalo, Irish tenors and the nickel cup of coffee, the clothesline is virtually becoming extinct. And with it goes the greatest communications medium the world has ever known.

When I was a kid, the neighbors stretched a clothesline the day they moved in. And we watched and learned. "How many of them are there? Boys or girls? Ages? Do they have nice underwear?" (Mama always said you could judge a woman by the underwear she hung and her character by the way she acted when her clothesline broke.)

By the time I had a home of my own, I could read Monday's wash like a gypsy reads tea leaves.

New diapers: "She brought the baby home."

Navy bell-bottoms: "His leave came through."

Extra sheets: "The in-laws from Kansas City."

Sleeping bags: "She finally found a camp to take those boys."

Blankets: "Stay away. They've got the virus again."

Training pants: "Well, it's about time."
Curtains and slipcovers: "She starts earlier every year."
Wading boots and fishing nets: "I'd leave the bum!"
Bathroom wall-to-wall carpet: "Status seekers!"

The clothesline was more than a flapping news bulletin. It was a little game housewives played. The women used to run a footrace to see who could get their wash out on the line first. If the sun ever rose on an empty clothesline, I think it had something to do with the success or the failure of your marriage. At least, it seemed that way.

It was also a test of skill and endurance to see how swiftly you could transfer a pair of steaming long johns to the clothesline in sub-zero temperatures without having them freeze in the basket in a cross-legged position.

As for me, it was group therapy . . . a lull in the busy day . . . a wave and a hello . . . a breath of fresh air . . . a glance upward at the sky . . . the smell of rain . . . the chill winds of winter to come . . . the fluffed-up chenille and the sweet-scented sheets that would never see an iron.

Why, if I had a clothesline today, I wouldn't be going crazy over the suitcases airing on my neighbor's patio. I'd have known before they did whether they were going or coming.

—April 20, 1967

ACKNOWLEDGMENTS

We gratefully acknowledge the publishers and writers who granted permission to reprint the material in this book. In a few cases, it was not possible to trace the original authors. We would like to be able to credit these authors if they would contact us by writing to Zondervan, 5300 Patterson Ave., S.E., Grand Rapids, MI 49530.

Terry Beck, "The Jubilee Agreement." Reprinted with permission of author.

Valerie Bell, "How Wilma 'Younged'." Taken from *A Well-Tended Soul.* Copyright © 1996 by Valerie Bell. Used by permission of Zondervan.

Evelyn Bence, "Last Night, Tonight." From *The Promise,* published by C. R. Gibson company © 1987 by Evelyn Bence. Used by permission of the author.

Suzanne Berne, "Perfect Mornings, Perfect Memories." Suzanne Berne is a novelist who lives near Boston. Used by permission of the author.

Erma Bombeck, "The American Clothesline—April 20, 1967." *Forever Erma* © 1996 by the Estate of Erma Bombeck. Reprinted with permission of Andrews and McNeel Publishing. All rights reserved.

Kim Boulton with Chris Wave, "Da Big Chair." Reprinted from *Finding God between a Rock and a Hard Place* by Lil Copan and Elisa Fryling. Used by permission of Shaw Books, an imprint of WaterBrook Press, Colorado Springs, CO 80920. All rights reserved.

Dale Hanson Bourke, "Holiday Memories." Taken from *Everyday Miracles* Copyright © 1999 Broadman & Holman Publishers. All rights reserved. Used by permission.

———. "It Will Change Your Life." Taken from *Everyday Miracles.* Copyright © 1999. Broadman & Holman Publishers. All rights reserved. Used by permission.

————. "Letting Go." Used by permission of Dale Hanson Bourke. Originally published in *Sacred Surprises* © 1987 Word Publishing.

Anne Bradstreet, *To My Dear and Loving Husband.*

Susan Branch, "Library Days." Taken from *The Summer Book from the Heart of the Home* copyright © 1995 by Susan Stewart Branch. Published by Little, Brown and Company.

Jill Briscoe, "Knowing When to Unload." Reprinted with permission of author.

Janice Chaffee, "Jaci's Story." Taken from *One Silent Night,* Copyright © 2000 by Janice Chaffee. Published by Harvest House Publishers, Eugene, Oregon 97404. Used by permission.

Patsy Clairmont, "Half-Pint." Taken from *God Uses Cracked Pots* by Patsy Clairmont, a Focus on the Family book published by Tyndale House. Copyright © 1991 by Patsy Clairmont. All rights reserved. International copyright secured. Used by permission.

Cathy Conger, "Celestial Symphony." A poet and freelance writer, Cathy lives with her family in Wisconsin Rapids, Wisconsin. Reprinted with permission of author.

————. "in the wee small hours of the morning." A poet and freelance writer, Cathy Conger has been a MOPS Mentor/speaker for eight years. Her most recent book of poetry is *In the Wee Small Hours of the Morning.* Reprinted with permission of author.

Christopher de Vinck, "The Magic Sound of Poetry." Taken from *The Book of Moonlight* by Christopher de Vinck. Copyright © 1998 by Christopher de Vinck. Used by permission of Zondervan.

Gwendolyn Mitchell Diaz, "A Mammoth Memory." Taken from *The Adventures Of Mighty Mom* by Gwendolyn Mitchell Diaz; RiverOak Publishing, a division of Honor Books. Copyright © 1999 by Gwendolyn Mitchell Diaz. Used by permission. All rights reserved.

Emily Dickinson, "'Hope' is the thing with feathers." Reprinted by permission of the publishers and the Trustees of Amherst College from *The Poems of Emily Dickinson,* Thomas H. Johnson, ed., Cambridge, Mass.: The Belknap Press of Harvard University Press, Copyright © 1951, 1955, 1979 by the President and Fellows of Harvard College.

————. "I dwell in Possibility." Reprinted by permission of the publishers and the Trustees of Amherst College from *The Poems of Emily Dickinson,* Thomas H. Johnson, ed., Cambridge, Mass.: The Belknap Press of Harvard University Press, Copyright © 1951, 1955, 1979 by the President and Fellows of Harvard College.

————. "There is no Frigate like a book." Reprinted by permission of the publishers and the Trustees of Amherst College from *The Poems of Emily Dickinson,* Thomas H. Johnson, ed., Cambridge, Mass.: The Belknap Press of Harvard University Press, Copyright © 1951, 1955, 1979 by the President and Fellows of Harvard College.

Elisabeth Elliott, "Neither Foreigner nor Savage." From *The Savage My Kinsman,* © 1961 and 1989 by Elisabeth Elliot. Published by Servant Publications, Box 8617, Ann Arbor, Michigan, 48107. Used with permission.

Shannon El-Sokkary , "Our-Sized Thanksgiving." Used with permission of author.

Mary Cooper Feliz, "Mixed Paints." Mary Feliz is the mother of two sons. A retired public relations professional, she is now working on a young adult novel. Reprinted with permission of the author.

Gloria Gaither, "Metamorphosis." Originally published in *Hands across the Seasons.* Used by permission.

Ellen Goodman, "Beat the Clock." © 1987, The Boston Globe Newspaper Co. The Washington Post Writers Group. Reprinted with permission.

Ruth Bell Graham, "Watch O'er My Flock." Reprinted with permission of author.

Robin Jones Gunn, "Like Mother, Like Daughter." Excerpted from *Mothering by Heart* © 1994 by Robin Jones Gunn. Used by permission of Multnomah Publishers, Inc.

Maida Heatter, excerpt from "Ah, There's Good News Tonight." From *Christmas Memories with Recipes,* edited by Marion L. Waxman. Copyright 1988 by Maida Heatter. Copyright © 1988 by Book-of-the-Month Club, Inc. Reprinted by permission of Farrar, Straus and Giroux, LLC.

Liz Curtis Higgs, "The Bombing of Newport Beach." Reprinted by permission of Thomas Nelson Publishers from the book, *Help! I'm Laughing and I Can't Get Up,* copyright 1998 by Liz Curtis Higgs.

————. "A Hairy Story." Reprinted by permission of Thomas Nelson Publishers from the book, *Help! I'm Laughing and I Can't Get Up,* copyright 1998 by Liz Curtis Higgs.

Amy Imbody, "Cincinnati!." Used with permission of author.

————. "High and Holy Work." Used with permission of author.

————. "Night Feedings." Used with permission of author.

Patsy Y. Iwasaki, "Kellie, My Maiden Warrior." Used with permission of author.

Mary Jensen, "Relearning Simplicity." Excerpted from *Still Life* © 1997 by Mary Jensen. Used by permission of Multnomah Publishers, Inc.

————. "A Time for Pearls." Taken from *First We Have Coffee and Then We Talk.* Copyright © 1995. Harvest House Publishers.

Louise Tucker Jones, "Guardian for All Time." Reprinted with permission from *Angels on Earth* magazine (January/February 1995). Copyright © 1994 by Guideposts, Carmel, New York 10512. Used by permission.

————. "I Want to Be Like Jay." From *Guideposts* (February 1995). Copyright © 1994 by Guideposts, Carmel, New York 10512. Used by permission.

Jo Kadlecek, "Mama's Pride." Taken from *Winter Flowers* by Jo Kadlecek. (Broadman & Holman Publishers, Nashville, 2001). All rights reserved. Used by permission.

Helen Keller, "The Story of My Life." Excerpt from *The Story of My Life.* Reproduced by permission of Hodder and Stoughton Limited.

Heather Harpham Kopp, "People Call It Camping." Taken from *I Stole God from Goody Two-Shoes.* (Eugene, OR: Harvest House Publishers 1994). Reprinted with permission.

Carol Kuykendall, "Sprinkles of Grace." Reprinted with permission of author.

Anne Morrow Lindbergh, "Hour of Gold, Hour of Lead." Excerpt from *Hour of Gold, Hour of Lead: Diaries and Letters of Anne Morrow Lindbergh,* copyright © 1973 by Anne Morrow Lindbergh, used by permission of Harcourt, Inc.

Anna Frances Lipinski, "The Creek." Reprinted with permission from *Welcome Home,* journal of the non-profit organization Mothers at Home www.mah.org.

Joy MacKenzie, "Lessons in a Goldfish Bowl." Taken from *Friends through Thick and Thin* by Sue Buchanan; Joy MacKenzie; Gloria L. Gaither; Peggy Benson. Copyright © 1998 by Gloria Gaither, Sue Buchanan, Peggy Benson, and Joy Mackenzie. Used by permission of Zondervan.

Karen Burton Mains, "'I Want to Write!'" Karen Burton Mains is co-director of Mainstay Ministries, which is dedicated to creating unforgettable Sundays. Reprinted with permission of author.

Joyce Maynard, "Our Mess Is Growing on Me." Longtime columnist and mother of three, Joyce Maynard is the author of *Domestic Affairs*, among many other works. Reprinted with permission.

Elisa Morgan, "God Remembers." Reprinted with permission of author.

———. "Helpful Hurts." Reprinted with permission of author.

Ruth Page, "Gardening as Therapy." From *Ruth Page's Gardening Journal*. Copyright © 1989 by the National Gardening Association. Illustrations copyright © 1989 by Bonnie Acker. Reprinted by permission of Houghton Mifflin Co. All rights reserved.

Chonda Pierce, "Radioactive Tomatoes." Taken from *It's Always Darkest before the Fun Comes Up* by Chonda Pierce. Copyright © 1998 by Chonda Pierce. Used by permission of Zondervan.

Anna Quindlen, "Pregnant in New York." From *Living Out Loud* by Anna Quindlen, copyright © 1987 by Anna Quindlen. Used by permission of Random House, Inc.

———. "Tag Sale." From *Living Out Loud* by Anna Quindlen, copyright © 1987 by Anna Quindlen. Used by permission of Random House, Inc.

Sharon Growney Seals, "Around My Mother's Table." Published in *Welcome Home*, November 1996. Visit their website at www.mah.org. Reprinted by permission of author.

Luci Shaw, "The Book of Nature." Taken from *Water My Soul* Copyright © 1998 by Luci Shaw. Used by permission of Zondervan.

———. "Her Frozen Soul Was Thawed." Taken from *Water My Soul* by Luci Shaw. Copyright © 1998 by Luci Shaw. Used by permission of Zondervan.

————. "Possess your soul in patience." Reprinted from *The Angles of Light* © 2000 by Luci Shaw. Used by permission of Shaw Books, an imprint of WaterBrook Press, Colorado Springs, CO 80920. All rights reserved.

————. "Spice." Reprinted from *Polishing the Petoskey Stone* © 1990 by Luci Shaw. Used by permission of Shaw Books, an imprint of WaterBrook Press, Colorado Springs, CO 80920. All rights reserved.

Karen Dona Stuart, "Strawberries and Cream: A Lesson in Diplomacy." Used with permission of the author.

Luci Swindoll, "Treasure in the Trash." Taken from *Stories of Hope for a Healthy Soul* copyright © 1999 by the Livingstone Corporation. Used by permission of Zondervan.

Elizabeth Traff, "Autumn Whispers." Used with permission of author.

————. "Winter's Wood." Used with permission of author.

John Trent with Erin M. Healy, "Margaret's Story." Reprinted from *My Mother's Hands.* Copyright © 2000 by WaterBrook Press. Used by permission of WaterBrook Press, Colorado Springs, CO. All rights reserved.

Ingrid Trobisch, "Being a Keeper." Orginally published in *Keeper of Springs* by Ingrid Trobisch. Multnomah Publishers. Reprinted by permission of author.

Sheila Walsh, "Telling the Truth." Taken from *Living Fearlessly* by Sheila Walsh. Copyright © 2001 by Sheila Walsh. Used by permission of Zondervan.

Deena Lee Wilson, "That's My Boy!" Excerpted from *A Mom's Legacy,* Copyright © 1999. Gospel Light/Regal Books, Ventura, CA 93003. Used by permission.

What Is MOPS?

MOPS stands for Mothers of Preschoolers, a program designed to encourage mothers with children under school age through relationships and resources. These women come from different backgrounds and lifestyles, yet have similar needs and a shared desire to be the best mothers they can be!

A MOPS group provides a caring, accepting atmosphere for today's mother of preschoolers. Here she has an opportunity to share concerns, explore areas of creativity and hear instruction that equips her for the responsibilities of family and community. The MOPS group also includes MOPPETS, a loving, learning experience for children.

Approximately 2,700 groups meet in churches throughout the United States, Canada, and 19 other countries, to meet the needs of more than 100,000 women. Many more mothers are encouraged by MOPS resources, including *MOMSense* radio and magazine, the MOPS web site, and MOPS brand books.

Find out how MOPS International can help you become part of the MOPS♥to♥MOM Connection:

MOPS International
P.O. Box 102200
Denver, CO 80250–2200
Phone 1-800-929-1287 or 303-733-5353
E-mail: Info@MOPS.org
Web site: http://www.MOPS.org
To learn how to start a MOPS group,
Call 1-888-910-MOPS.
For MOPS products call the MOPShop
1-888-545-4040.

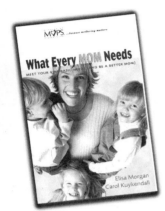

What Every Mom Needs
Meet Your Nine Basic Needs
(and Be a Better Mom)
Elisa Morgan & Carol Kuykendall

After more than twenty years of research and experience with moms, MOPS has identified your nine basic needs as a mother: significance, identity, growth, intimacy, instruction, help, recreation, perspective, and hope. *What Every Mom Needs* is an invaluable resource for women who long to expand their personal horizons and become better mothers at the same time.

Softcover 0-310-21920-5

What Every Child Needs
Meet Your Child's Nine Needs for Love
Elisa Morgan & Carol Kuykendall

Details in a warm and nurturing style the nine needs of every child: security, affirmation, family, respect, play, guidance, discipline, independence, and hope. Don't miss the great stories, helpful hints, and practical suggestions that will help you recognize and meet these needs in the life of your child.

Softcover 0-310-23271-6

Children Change a Marriage
What Every Couple Needs to Know
Elisa Morgan & Carol Kuykendall

This book helps new parents and soon-to-be parents understand the transition from husband and wife to mom and dad, and helps them establish the foundation for a fulfilling and vital marriage relationship. Formerly titled *When Husband and Wife Become Mom and Dad.*

Softcover 0-310-24299-1

Coming in January 2002

Make Room for Daddy
A Mom's Guide to Letting Dad Be Dad
Elisa Morgan & Carol Kuykendall

This book will help moms understand the differences in and importance of fathering and give them perspective on how to let dads be dads.

Softcover 0-310-24044-1

ZONDERVAN™

GRAND RAPIDS, MICHIGAN 49530
www.zondervan.com

MOTHERS OF
M♥PS®
PRESCHOOLERS
...because mothering matters

Little Books for Busy Moms

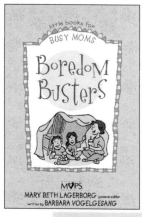

Softcover 0-310-23997-4

Softcover 0-310-23515-4

Softcover 0-310-23514-6

Softcover 0-310-24178-2

Softcover 0-310-23511-1

Softcover 0-310-23999-0

Softcover 0-310-23513-8

ZONDERVAN™

GRAND RAPIDS, MICHIGAN 49530

www.zondervan.com

M♥PS, *resources from* Zonder**kidz**

Little Jesus, Little Me
Written by Doris Rikkers
Illustrated by Dorothy Stott
Board Book 0-310-23205-8

My Busy, Busy Day
Written by Kelly Kim
Photographed by
Bender & Bender Photography, Inc.
Board Book 0-310-23206-6

Morning, Mr. Ted!
Written by Crystal Bowman
Illustrated by Liz Conrad
Board Book 0-310-70060-4

**See the Country,
See the City**
Written by Crystal Bowman
Illustrated by Pam Thomson
Hardcover 0-310-23210-4

Boxes, Boxes Everywhere!
Written by Crystal Bowman
Illustrated by Jane Schettle
Board Book 0-310-70062-0